ENGINEER YOUR CAREER

Here is the first book for your
Professional Engineer library - Its a
good Read!!

Love you Buddy
Opa

ENGINEER YOUR CAREER

A COMPLETE GUIDE TO
LANDING A JOB IN ENGINEERING

THOMAS A. ANDERSON, P.E.

First printing 2019
ISBN 978-0-578-47544-8

Cover image ID 26089173 © Jason Winter | Dreamstime.com

*This book is dedicated to all those who change
the lives of engineers by living as an example
and by empowering others for greatness.*

Acknowledgments

In preparing *Engineer Your Career*, I wish to acknowledge my indebtedness to the wholehearted cooperation and vast experience of my mentors and colleagues:

Don Buszinski	Jared Kaufman
Jeff Buszinski	David McCullough
Robert Draper	Mark Miller
Tom Glassbrenner	Fabrizio Rambaldi
Brandt Hathaway	Ralph Raurk
David Irvine	Carl Sutherland

Sincerest thanks are also due to the following people for their invaluable help in compiling this book:

Teddi Black	Crystal Morrison
Bonnie Budzowski	Nader Mowlaee
Mel Butcher	Elisabeth Nilsson
Deana Coddaire	George Robinson
Kyle Elliot	Stephanie Slocum
Kathi Finch	Robynn Storey
Madison Lux	Woodrow Winchester III

Contents

Introduction

Your education is not enough to land you the career you want.

As a sophomore in engineering school, I had a part-time job in the engineering computer lab, and I was anxious and bored. I knew I needed the experience to move forward, but I didn't know where to get it. My idea of an engineer bounced between an astronaut and a bridge designer on a golf course. So, I started picking my professors' brains. I did some online research about the places they worked and the responsibilities they performed.

One professor, in particular, had a job designing solid oxide fuel cells. Out of all the engineers I knew, he had by far the coolest job. So I started begging. Every time I saw my professor, I would ask, "Can I have an internship?" He always replied, "I will look into it." After months of begging, he finally came to me with an answer.

It was "no."

Unfortunately, the solid oxide fuel cell division where he worked was being shut down—no room at the inn. However, my professor did offer me an alternative. He said that a colleague from the Engineers' Society had been asking him to perform some heat transfer calculations for them; he said I was capable of performing the calculations, and he could check them before he submitted them.

This opportunity was exciting. It didn't pay a dime, but I didn't care. It was something to put on my résumé besides "sitting in the computer lab."

I completed a few calculations, reviewed with my professor, and we submitted the work. *Now what?* I wondered. *Where is this going to go?* I hatched a plan. I'd show up at the engineering company and simply tell them they needed an intern. It was my best chance of landing a position, and frankly, the pay didn't matter because I needed the experience.

One weekday morning I showed up at their office. "Hello, I'm Thomas, your new intern." Confused but courteous, they asked who sent me. "My professor," I replied. They stared blankly at each other, wondering what to do. Finally, they said, "Yeah, ok. Let's find you a desk."

It turns out they needed my help and were able to pay me. I was able to go to the office during the day and switch my classes to the evening. It couldn't have worked out better.

How did I do it? Did I go to a prestigious school? No. Did I have a 4.0? No. Did I fill out hundreds of online applications? No. I used perseverance, confidence, networking, and communication. I convinced them they needed me, and that I was worth the gamble.

As a mechanical engineer, I love what I do. I design equipment to heat, melt, carburize, spheroidize, quench, anneal, and treat all kinds of metals, ceramics, glass, and many other materials. Designs I have created over the years have impacted thousands of people's lives. Equipment I have designed helps create a better world with more sustainability, less maintenance, and lower energy usage. I have been blessed to contribute to multiple industries all around the world.

I have enjoyed all of my tenure in engineering, but the last couple of years have been the best of my professional career. I received my Professional Engineering license, accepted a fantastic position at a reputable engineering firm, landed a promotion, gave speeches to dozens of organizations, published technical papers, and presented in front of hundreds of engineers. I also made an excellent decision: I decided to mentor young engineers. Throughout my career, I have always tried to help young engineers learn the same lessons I have. My message is simple: I don't want you to make some of the mistakes I have, and I thoroughly enjoy seeing you succeed.

If you are a young engineer, I don't have to tell you that making the transition from engineering school to a career is difficult. Some companies will provide training for you and strive to help you with your future. Most don't. It doesn't help that you have been "syllabized" by your university and have no idea how to get your career off the ground.

You, like many others, may be lacking basic nontechnical skills, like problem-solving, decision-making, and the ability to prioritize tasks. When I began coaching, I thought to myself, "If I can provide the knowledge and lessons I have learned over the years, I can help other engineers succeed." I had no idea just how many young engineers were looking for guidance. The more I helped, the more I realized just how many of you needed support.

As a result, I started spending my spare time speaking to engineering students, giving presentations at universities, conducting coaching calls, posting content for engineers, and answering every question I could on LinkedIn. I consistently answered the same questions: "Is an engineering career just like college?" "How many calculations will I be doing every day?" "What's the best résumé?" "Can you look at my LinkedIn profile?" These questions led to the creation of my website, **www.EngineerYourCareer.net**. I created and posted content to help engineers answer their questions about engineering…but it wasn't enough.

After helping hundreds of engineers and responding to even more questions, one thing was clear. Young engineers are asking the wrong questions. For example: "What tricks do I need to land a job?" "What field is best for landing a position?" "What certifications do I need to work in the _____ industry?" These questions do not reflect the path that young engineers need to take to land a career they enjoy. So, I began to ask myself, *how can I create an all-encompassing guide to help young engineers achieve their career goals?* The answer is this book—a complete guide to landing and starting an excellent engineering career.

I want to give you the keys to success. To learn what I learned…and more. I want you to have the resources to land the career you dreamed of when you decided to go to engineering school. I want your education to be well worth all the money, time, and effort you put into it. *Engineer Your Career* was created to help you do just that: Show you how to land an engineering job and get your career off the ground.

Where are you right now in your path? Are you looking for your first internship? Do you know how to prepare for graduation? Graduated and still haven't landed a job? Have you filled out hundreds of online job applications only to get a call or two? Landed a few interviews but fell short of being hired?

In this book, I break down difficult early career issues into manageable, common sense approaches. I discuss key concepts that will help you develop a résumé, connect with hiring managers and technical recruiters, ace interviews, and start the career of your dreams. This book gives you all of the information you need to start a successful engineering career. It contains strategies to improve your non-technical skills, as well as ideas for goal setting, networking, and even public speaking. Becoming successful always requires a practical approach.

This book is the key to finding that approach…and it will provide you with everything you need to *Engineer Your Career.*

How to Use This Book

How can you use this book to land your dream career? I use a simple step-by-step chronological approach, including specific statistics, stories, outlines, and templates to show you a clear method for your job search. You may be tempted to leaf through the book and go straight to the résumé section, but I encourage you to read and follow the entire process.

Chapter 1: Understand the Truth about Engineering – Teaches you the critical and straightforward truth about your engineering education and what most students and graduates struggle to understand.

Chapter 2: Recognize Your Purpose – Helps you to identify what you are looking for professionally. What do you want in your career? What industry should you pursue? Who do you want to help?

Chapter 3: Plan Your Career – Gives you the basics toward a short-term career plan. It shows you what you should consider and why it's so important.

Chapter 4: Identify What Employers Want – Shows you the critical hard and soft skills you need to recognize, practice and use to land the career of your dreams.

Chapter 5: Craft an Excellent Résumé – Provides a straightforward approach to creating a résumé as a student or recent graduate, using a guide and a template.

Chapter 6: Get Networking – Shows you how to communicate, sell yourself, and how to network.

Chapter 7: Reach Out and Gain Opportunities – Shows you how and where to land contacts with hiring managers, colleagues, and technical recruiters.

Chapter 8: Ace Interviews – Gives you the top questions asked at interviews and how to answer them. It covers important topics such as interview flow, phone interviews, what to do, what not to do, and how to follow up after an interview.

Chapter 9: Accept an Offer – This section provides you with the dos and don'ts to receiving an offer. It lists step-by-step what you need to do.

Chapter 10: Create an Amazing Career – Takes you through the important concepts of building relationships, focusing on solutions, lifelong learning, and facing failure.

Chapter 11: Continue Your Education – Looks at the most popular and most utilized engineering certifications and licenses.

Chapter 13: Templates – Provides multiple templates for some of those exciting and sometimes challenging tasks you will undoubtedly encounter while building your career: cover letter, cold emailing, thank you letter, offer negotiation, offer acceptance, and resignation.

This book will help you to get your engineering career off the ground and show you how to make it the best it can be. Are you ready to *Engineer Your Career*?

1

Understand the Truth about Engineering

"As in real life, complex engineering designs demand a pragmatic approach."
–Haresh Sippy

You've spent tens of thousands of dollars on education, as well as countless hours learning and preparing for an engineering career you may not know much about. Years ago, an engineering degree was a privilege. If you were lucky enough to be accepted to college and graduate, you knew you'd land a job, and what your engineering career would be like even before you began. You could expect a nice starting salary, a pension, a bright future, and maybe even lifetime employment.

Now, thousands of universities make it possible for anyone to attempt an engineering degree. These days, an engineering degree does not get you ahead of the curve; it merely allows for an equal starting position. Salaries are down, and student debt is up. Young engineers are starting in the workforce without any professional experience. Nowadays, an engineering degree is more expensive, and the return on investment is down significantly. In fact, between 2009 and 2018, national student debt doubled to $1.465 trillion! (Chapman, 2018)

The engineering education system prevents curiosity, is rigid, and frankly, does not prepare you for the workforce. How could it? Engineering firms specialize in different industries, services, and technologies. You've gained an understanding of engineering principles, but how do you translate that knowledge to a long, successful career? As they approach graduation, many students feel the pressure of getting a job. *I've done what I've been told,* they think, *and now I deserve a huge paycheck and great benefits.* This thinking could not be further from the truth. The truth is they are simply now in a position to start learning about the business of engineering.

Here is the good news:

- You are the largest, most educated generation of engineers to enter the workforce—and you are in high demand.
- Engineering occupations are projected to grow 7 percent from 2016 to 2026. That's approximately 194,300 new jobs. (Statistics, 2018)
- Industry experts expect a national shortage of 500,000 technical workers by 2020. (Directory, 2018)

- Engineering services will be in demand in various areas, such as the rebuilding of infrastructure, renewable energy, oil and gas extraction, and robotics. (Statistics, 2018)
- Research conducted by LinkedIn identified the STEM skills most in demand, including expertise in cloud computing, data mining and statistical analysis, and writing smartphone applications. (Directory, 2018)

The bad news:

- You are unprepared, professionally immature, probably in debt, and often seen as a burden in the workplace.
- Older generations don't have any sympathy for your situation and often give "tough love." They get frustrated with your attitude and demand respect for their professional sacrifices in a career they may or may not enjoy. No one expects you to follow their example, but you do have to recognize that experience is fundamental to developing your knowledge and skills.

After Your Engineering Degree

If you are like most people, you spent four+ years of your life—and tens of thousands of dollars—to attend college, hoping to land a high-paying career you love. Unfortunately, your education is not enough. Below are the important items you need to know about your education.

Your grades are not as important as you think. In college, I was a straight B student. I don't brag about it. I spent the majority of my time in college working at an internship to keep the ramen noodles on the table. I needed the money, but I also knew that the experience I was getting at the internship was essential.

Needless to say, A's are better. I wish I had more. But if you're pouring all your efforts into getting straight A's, you may be missing opportunities like experience, volunteering, student organizations, networking, or even making new friends. All of these things are critical to a résumé, an interview, and life.

If you get a degree in engineering, you have to become an engineer, right? It makes sense. However, there are hundreds of different types of jobs that people with engineering degrees can fill. Within a particular field, you can do anything from maintenance to sales, and from software to marketing. Although your degree is specific, your career doesn't have to be. Your experiences make you who you are—not the degree on your diploma.

Here are some basics you need to know:

You never really graduate.

When you put on your cap and gown, celebrate. But keep in mind, if you want to excel in your career, you have to keep learning. You need to stay current within your field. It will also keep you from getting bored.

The job is not about the degree.

Your degree gives you the opportunity to discover and hone your skills. It is up to you to decide how to capitalize on them. Young engineers often look at their degrees in terms of what they can get from them. It is much more useful to look at how you can use those skills to benefit your company and your career.

You will never use the majority of what you learned.

Sad but true. The specific field you chose will determine what subjects you will use. Once you graduate, chances are that all the equations you worked so hard to memorize will disappear. The problems you face will be "open book." Most of the effort at work will be remote from facts, figures, and sometimes, even logic. You will be dealing with relationships, clients, company-specific systems, and mostly problem-solving.

Engineers need creativity.

Creativity isn't limited to playing an instrument or painting a picture. Creativity is needed to design a new component, fit large things into small spaces, come up with a scientific theory, or write software. It's about using your imagination and brainstorming to create something that doesn't exist. Successful engineers are creative.

Luck is involved.

Despite what most parents say, you cannot be anything you want. Hard work is not the only influence on success. Without 20/20 vision, you can't be a pilot. If you have a fear of heights, you can't be an astronaut. There's luck involved in succeeding. That doesn't mean you shouldn't try. It means you need to prepare for failure and be ready to face it. Don't miss a lucky break.

It isn't about the money.

Your mission, like many others, may be to find a high-paying job. However, you need to know how to manage money properly. If you haven't already, take some time to learn about budgets, savings, and investing. Take it seriously. If you do make some money, you will have something to show for it. As Will Rogers so aptly put it: "The quickest way to double your money is to fold it over and put it back in your pocket."

More degrees do not mean more money.

If you are not sure what to do next, the *last* thing you should do is stay in school. Education is not always a safe bet. Advanced degrees only provide career advancement when they align with an opportunity. If you decide to go straight through to your master's degree and *then* enter the workforce, you'll end up competing with bachelor-degreed students for the same money. Why? You both have limited experience. Instead, try to work for a company that will pay for a master's degree. You will both benefit.

Myths about Engineers

Often, engineers are portrayed in a not-so-flattering light. Try a search result for "engineers are" and see what comes up:

- Dull people
- Boring
- Dumb
- Weird
- Cheap
- Arrogant

Thanks, search engines! Young engineers are often stereotyped. We are different. It's important to understand engineers. After all, you are one.

MYTH: Engineers do not communicate well.

The myth is true for some, but if you want to be at the top of the ladder, you need to have excellent communication skills. More and more engineers are becoming leaders. Communication is the key.

MYTH: Engineers mostly do calculations.

A day doesn't go by that I don't use my calculator, but I rarely do high-level calculations. This is not true for all engineers. Your specific role dictates how many calculations you complete in an average week. Remember, you may be calculating the same thing over and over based on different parameters. Why not use a spreadsheet? Most of my time is spent problem-solving, reviewing designs, checking budgets, attending meetings, and completing paperwork.

MYTH: Engineers can fix anything.

Most engineers can tell you principles of how your toaster or microwave work, but engineers are *not* your local repairperson. They are designers using the principles of science to solve problems.

MYTH: Engineers love math.

Engineers need to be good at math, but it does not mean they like it. Math is a critical part of engineering—but certainly not all of it.

MYTH: Engineering is boring.

Boring depends on where you are working and what you are doing. Sure, some parts can be boring, but it depends on what excites you. If you are using creativity to solve complex problems, you aren't likely to be bored.

MYTH: Engineering is tough.

Engineering is relentless. Day-to-day, project-to-project—the tasks, duties, challenges, and parameters change. Engineering is a constant problem-solving process. Many problems happen at the same time.

> The biggest myth in engineering is that your technical skill competencies will determine your level of success. There are many, many technically competent (and even genius-level) engineers. That's one of many reasons that in reality, your people skills will determine how far you are able to go in your career.
>
> You must be technically competent to succeed as an engineer. However, an average engineer with excellent people skills – specifically those related to storytelling, public speaking, motivating others, and creating relationships – will almost always be more successful in any measurable way than an engineer with amazing technical skills but mediocre people skills.
>
> **Stephanie Slocum, P.E.** – Founder, Engineers Rising LLC and author of the book *She Engineers*

What Do Engineers Do?

Engineers answer the question of how. How do we get to the moon? How do we cross a river? How do we fly like a bird? We design, create, and innovate using the scientific method. An engineer works between scientific discoveries and the applications that meet societal and consumer needs. We are problem solvers.

We utilize the tools of science and mathematics to produce and analyze designs, and test how machines, structures, or systems operate. We monitor the quality and efficiency of processes and products.

To develop products, engineers must consider several factors. For example, in developing an industrial robot, engineers must precisely determine and specify the functional requirements. They design and test the robot's components, integrate those components to produce the design, and evaluate the design's overall effectiveness, cost, reliability, and safety. Processes like this apply to the development of virtually every product you can think of—metals, phones, power plants, airplanes, and children's toys. You name it, it's probably been engineered in some fashion.

In addition to design and development, many engineers work in testing, production, and maintenance. They supervise factories, determine the causes of component failures, test manufactured products for proper quality, and estimate the time and cost required to complete projects.

Engineering is quite possibly the most underrated occupation group. We build homes, offices, roads, bridges, hospitals, communication lines, waterworks, power systems, and other infrastructures that make our lives possible. We created our modern society. We are important—*very* important.

What Makes a Great Engineer?

Why did Edison continue after 1,000 failures? Why did Ford pursue his idea of a motorized car while everybody else was satisfied with horse-drawn carriages? What led Leonardo Da Vinci to become the biggest visionary of all time?

Engineers are responsible for many of the greatest inventions and technology that makes our existence possible. Do you have what it takes to join this elite club of creative thinkers?

Strong analytics – Analytical skills are required to examine problems and think of ways to improve.

Passion – Passion, drive, and motivation all lead to an attitude that will bring you success.

Communication skills – Complex problem-solving requires concise and accurate communication with your co-workers, boss, clients, vendors, and the public. You need to be able to translate your specialized knowledge into terms everyone can understand.

Attention to detail – Engineering projects are complex. A small mistake during planning, development, or construction can lead to failure. A failed project may lose money, or worse yet, injure someone.

Creativity – Solving new problems requires creativity for solutions. Thinking outside the box is critical to solving unique problems.

Logical thinking – Great engineers can make sense of complex systems, understand how things work, and how problems arise.

Team player – Engineers rarely work alone. Working collaboratively with different types of people is an everyday event. Applying these people skills to communications helps to simplify and prioritize issues. You need the character and integrity to allow people to trust and rely on you to all work together efficiently.

Technical knowledge – A great engineer has vast amounts of technical knowledge. They use this knowledge and apply it to different circumstances and issues.

Lifetime learning – Changes happen rapidly, and successful engineers stay on top of the latest technology, to keep a finger on the pulse of new research and ideas.

> While studying engineering, I took a lot of pride being interested in technology. Maybe this character trait was additionally fed by the lack of females in my profession. Being a female interested in programming or laboratory works always gave me the spotlight.
>
> When entering the industry, I struggled. I did not find the job I wanted – the academic, high-tech, research-oriented high-level internships I loved from studying did not have a

clear corresponding full-time engineering equivalent. I entered a trainee program, where I was given the opportunity to try out several jobs at a large OEM. Most of my peers and seniors did not take pride in technology the same way I did, and only a handful of people at the whole company worked with technology. Managers, production leaders, and sale force jobs circulated mostly around other people! My heroes, the development engineers, seldom got the spotlight, since engineers in management roles or a sales engineer landing a big deal always got the main spotlight.

So, a major myth I want to burst regarding engineering is the fact that our jobs are high-tech. Most engineers end up in a position where their engineering knowledge helps them understand the processes and products – but by the end of the day, their performance is measured on soft skills such as leadership, social, and integrity.

So, if you during studies feel discouraged that Thermo 2 is not sticking properly, remember that you will seldom be tested on this in real life. Listening and providing for the needs of others will make you as much of an office hero as being a killer in Thermo 2.

Elisabeth Nilsson – Podcast cohost STEMCAST, Chemical Engineer

Chapter 1—What You Learned

Now you know what engineers do, the common misconceptions of engineers and graduates, and what it takes to be a great engineer. You understand that your degree is not enough to land you the career you want. You have to work for it. But don't fret—the juice is worth the squeeze. Your career in engineering will provide a wide variety of benefits to your life. Now it's time to make some decisions. What is your dream engineering career? What type of career do you want? Who do you want to help? On to Chapter 2—Recognize Your Purpose.

Action Items:

- Write down the engineering activities that interest you. Maybe it's modeling, programming, stress analysis, or computational fluid dynamics.
- Write down the specific aspects of engineering that appeal to you. Are you most interested in design, prototyping, projects, business, sales, or research?

2

Recognize Your Purpose

*"The only way to do great work
is to love what you do."*
–Steve Jobs

What Do You Want? Really?

If you haven't decided which career path or field you would like to take, don't worry. This chapter is designed to describe some of the many possibilities and help you find your way.

What skills do young engineers need?

- Creative thinking
- Attention to detail
- Mathematics
- Communication

- Leadership
- Teamwork
- Organization
- Troubleshooting

What responsibilities did you enjoy in school? Did you enjoy working in groups? Tutoring? Were you a member of a student club? Did you enjoy the meetings? What about team projects? Do you like to work with others or alone? Do you enjoy organization? Each of the activities and tasks you enjoy is worth examining. They may be tied to your greatest strengths.

Holding a club meeting is part organization and part planning. Tutoring and working in groups involve leadership and teamwork. All of these activities are great clues as to where you want to go next.

What hobbies, activities, or tasks maintain your full attention? When do you get so engaged in an activity that you completely lose track of time? Brainstorming? Design sketches? Programming? AutoCAD? What do you love about the activity? What keeps you so engaged? Identify what holds your attention and aligns with your talents and interests. Be sure that these activities could easily become a work-related skill or even your next career.

Take a moment and ask yourself what your greatest strengths are. Do it proud. Give it thought. List things that you normally wouldn't say about yourself and brag a little bit. Need inspiration? Email friends and family members to find out what they find most inspiring about you. It may be awkward, but tell them why you're asking. You'll be surprised and fascinated by what you hear in response.

Once you've done this, take note of any themes or trends. How do you feel when you look at your list of strengths? Explore the possibilities.

You have created a list of talents and skills that will allow you to find the perfect career; employers want your skills and talents, too.

The following questions are designed to help you weigh the pros and cons of your dreams. The answers can be used to brainstorm how to achieve your goals, find solutions to your concerns and fears, and turn your dream into a reality.

- What do you envision for your engineering career?
- Can your dream become a career?
- Does your education align with your dream?
- What do you find so appealing about this dream?
- How would you feel if you could turn your dream into reality?
- What is negative about the dream?
- Does anything about this dream scare you?
- Are up to the challenge?
- Do you have support from others?

Discovering Your Purpose

The most satisfied engineers are not those with the most pay or benefits. They are the ones that have aligned their careers with their own unique purpose in life. Everyone has a purpose, but not everyone does the work to identify what that purpose is.

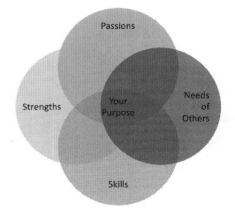

Your purpose can be broken down into four key categories: strengths, passions, skills, and the needs of others. The diagram shows the merging of these four concepts. If you can identify these categories and how they overlap with your purpose, you can get a strong idea of what your purpose might be.

We all have career dreams. However, most of the time we spend thinking about our dreams we either ignore reality, or simply do not pursue them. So, how do you find that dream?

What is of value to you? Who do you want to help? What makes you happy? What type of job do you want, what kind of people do you want to be around, and what knowledge do you wish to gain?

This last question is often asked in interviews, along with what your passions are, or what you like about engineering. Essentially, the interviewer wants to know: When things are not going your way, what lights your fire? What gets you motivated? What makes you want to go to work?"

Discovering your purpose is critical to finding a career that aligns with your passions. The following worksheets will help walk you through the steps of determining your purpose. This process can—and will—take some time. Put effort into it. Reflect on your answers. Challenge yourself. Your purpose is ultimately the most important part of starting your career.

STEP 1 – Passions

Answer the following questions in the area below.

What would you do if you won the lottery?

What activities do you enjoy?

Which activities get you excited?

What hobbies do you have?

What sparks your curiosity?

What do you do in your free time?

List your top 3 passions:

STEP 2 – Skills

Answer the following questions in the area below.

What have you been trained to do?

What skills do you have?

What projects did you excel in while at school? Enjoy?

List your top 3 skills:

STEP 3 – Strengths

Answer the following questions in the area below.
What thing do you do that receives praise?
What things come naturally?
Or give you the most satisfaction?

List your top 3 strengths:

STEP 4 – Needs of Others

Answer the following questions in the area below.

What are the problems you can solve for your audience?

What does your audience need?

Have you been paid to help others? What did you do?

List your top 3 needs:

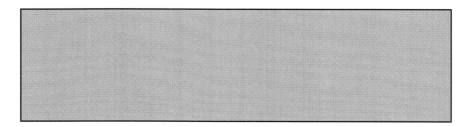

STEP 5 – Find the Overlap

It's time to brainstorm to align your career and your true purpose with your career path.

Top 3 Passions

Top 3 Skills

Top 3 Strengths

Top 3 Needs of Others

List 3 ways that your passions, strengths, skills, and needs of others overlap

Who will you help?

How will your career align with your purpose?

Choosing and Targeting Industries

Often, I hear the question, "Does ____ industry have opportunities right now?" And, while I don't say it, I want to answer: "Who cares?" Is this the deciding factor on where you will take your career—what's available now? Sounds like a great way to find a career you may hate. Your career choice is an important decision that will have a significant effect on your life. (Remember that there is little or no relationship between earnings and job satisfaction.)

Before you decide to pursue a particular industry within your engineering discipline, ask yourself this question: Can I see myself performing these duties all day, every day? When you choose a specific industry, make sure it's a good match for your interests, abilities, and purpose. You certainly don't want to design meat processing facilities if you're a vegetarian, or fire protection systems if you're a pyromaniac. Find an industry that matches your interests.

Be sure to complete extensive research about the industry you are considering by reading company websites and asking your contacts in-depth questions.

I have had great luck on LinkedIn finding and asking questions of other engineers about their industries. People love talking about themselves, so be sure to ask.

Research companies – Once you have found an industry that suits you, it's time to look at some companies. It's important to consider not only the reputation, but the size of different companies, the projects they work on, the problems they solve, and the culture.

Identify a few companies you would like to work for and do some research. Find these companies' career pages and regularly check for openings. Think about what about these companies inspires you to work for them.

Do careful research. How long have they been in business? Try contacting employees of the companies which you are interested in. How do they like what they do? What about past employees? Why did they leave? Has the company hired and let go numerous young people? Is the culture a fit for you?

Identify the job requirements – Once you've identified some companies that interest you, it's time to figure out if you have the qualifications and skills to handle the position. Where do you look? Job descriptions.

If a job description isn't specific enough to give you the details, here are a few things you can try:

- Connect and talk to people who have done the work. If you are looking to apply for a project engineering position, find some project engineers. The better you understand the job details and necessary skills, the easier it is to make a good impression during an interview.

- Get involved with engineering societies, clubs, conventions, and organizations: Professional gatherings and events can open up enormous opportunities for finding different job requirements.

- Volunteer. Investing time without pay isn't easy, but it is an excellent first step to getting your foot in the door and learning the ropes. Volunteering does not have to involve an employer. It can be beneficial to volunteer for work at an engineering club or society. It's a great place to get one-on-one conversations with engineering professionals in your area; maybe you could work together to accomplish a goal. Most of all, it's a connection that can last your entire career.

Any engineering position will require some on-the-job training to learn the specifics, but it's extremely important that you know the details of the position. The more the hiring manager believes you can do the job successfully, the more likely he or she is to hire you.

Expand opportunities – Unfortunately, you may not be able to land your dream career the first time around. Expand your opportunities by searching for companies and positions in multiple industries. Consider contract or temporary opportunities. These will strengthen your experience and may lead to full-time positions.

Location, Location, Location

Obtaining your career goals may require more experience than you currently have. Maybe you need more experience as an intern or a volunteer in a particular field. If your career interests are centrally located in one area, consider relocation before and during your application process. If you would like to work in a centrally located industry, such as Silicon Valley, it is much easier to make connections and attend interviews if you are living in the area.

Some people relish the idea of moving to a new city and meeting new people, while others hate the idea. If you're in the latter category, staying close to your loved ones may be an essential factor in your job search.

Value Proposition

"Value proposition refers to a business or marketing statement that a company uses to summarize why a consumer should buy a product or use a service. This statement convinces a potential consumer that one particular product or service will add more value or better solve a problem than other similar offerings will."
(Kenton, 2018)

Why as engineers do we need a value proposition? When engineers are trying to sell themselves, a value proposition statement can have significant effects on the outcome. A value proposition answers the following:

- How will you solve problems?
- How will you improve a process or product?
- What benefits can your employer expect?
- Why are you better than your competition?

A value proposition is an easy-to-understand, concise statement that tells the buyer, or in this case, a potential employer, exactly what problems you plan to solve and what benefits you have to offer. It's also a great way to make a first impression. So, how do you write a value proposition, you ask? Read on…

Pick a target.

Decide where you want your career to go and set a target for getting there. Targeting will help you become effective.

Identify your strengths.

What is the foundation for your value proposition? What strengths can help your buyer? Connect the dots for them. Consider their perspective and why they should hire you, promote you, or buy from you.

Use stories as evidence.

Use your success stories; your achievements will prove your strengths. They help make your proposition convincing.

Here are some examples*:

My skills as a mechanical engineer will increase your production, decrease overhead, and reduce maintenance.

Here are some of the high-level achievements I achieved at _____ that I plan to bring to your company:

- *Increased ____ production by 20%*
- *Decreased ____ maintenance costs by 35%*
- *Reduced ____ operating costs by 10%*

Are you looking for an entry-level engineer capable of meeting deadlines while saving you money and improving efficiencies?

As an electrical engineer, I will successfully design components with cost efficiency and accuracy. Below are the results I have achieved for _____:

- *Increased efficiency of _____ product by 20%*
- *Reduced prototyping budget by 10%*
- *Implemented a new quality assurance plan*

I am an innovative electrical engineer, and your company will undoubtedly benefit from my experiences.

I complete projects that meet the customer's needs and increase revenue— on time and on budget. My technical knowledge can help your customers solve complex issues and processes. I have a strong sense of ownership, personal accountability, and work beyond my duties to improve products. Never satisfied with my performance, I continually think of ways to improve designs, procurement, and execution. I am passionate about my career.

*Note: This is the same as the summary on the résumé template.

I stared at the green prison walls as the correctional officer's wand hovered over my body, looking for whatever metal had set off the metal detector as I had entered the facility. I had been tasked as the project engineering manager for a renovation of a steam line in this prison complex, and this was the first site visit, as well as my first time in a prison.

As the guard escorted us out into the yard, I remember him joking about the last prison riot at this particular facility, and reminding our team to stay close. As our team walked from building to building to review the existing conditions and determine a possible path for the new steam line, it felt like invisible eyes were on me. I was the only woman on the design team, and this particular prison housed predominately male offenders.

Normally, my employer focused on projects related to higher education. Now we were amid the Great Recession, so we'd needed to take some additional work. This project was mine.

Did I learn a lot? Yes. Did I ever want to work on a prison project again given a choice? Absolutely not.

Contrast this project with a university classroom building I was also designing at the time. The architect for the project was an old family friend, and the building would be used to teach students and do academic research.

Did I give my best performance, hit all milestones, and meet all engineering requirements (as well as pass all QA/QC checks with flying colors) on both of these projects? Yes.

Yet, the university building project turned out so well (despite some significant challenges during construction) that we got the call for the next, multi-million dollar building project with the same client. The extra effort I had been willing to put in – much of which was on a completely subconscious level – was because I was working in an area that matched my values. I had found my engineering "design passion," and it has shown in my work.

Stephanie Slocum, P.E. – Founder, Engineers Rising LLC and author of the book *She Engineers*.

Chapter 2—What You Learned

In Chapter 2, we worked together to find what you're looking for, which industries you'd like to target, and you learned that location is a crucial component. Now that you know what you are looking for, we can start to work on planning. Planning is a critical component of your job search as well as your career. A carefully considered plan can accelerate your job search and career.

Action Items:

- Complete the purpose worksheet. Spend some time with it and take it seriously.

- Compare your lists in Chapter 1. Do they match? Do your companies fit your industry? If not, consider adjusting. Remember, location is important, too.

- Do your skills and strengths match what it takes to be a great engineer? If not, no worries. You now know what you need to address.

3

Plan Your Career

"A goal without a plan is a wish."
–Antoine de Saint-Exupery

Career Planning

A career plan will help you determine your interests based on your skills, education, and desires. By developing a career plan, you can focus on what you want to do and how to get there. With your plan in mind, you can adequately showcase your skills and experiences both in your résumé, and talking with hiring managers. Clearly defining your goals can help you focus on realistic possibilities.

Before planning a career route, get to know yourself. Many people follow an established pattern of unhappiness and may not realize how or what other things they could be doing. Don't follow a familiar path. Make your own. Identifying your goals takes time and effort, but it is a vital process in any successful person's journey. According to the website Goalband:

- 83% of the U.S. population do not have goals.
- 92% of New Year's goals fail by Jan 15th.
- Those people with written goals are 50% more likely to succeed.
- Writing down a goal is a compelling motivator.
- Specific goals which are time-bound and measurable work best.

A career goal can be specific to a job within engineering, such as a project engineer, project manager, or sales engineer. On the other hand, the goal can be to work in a particular field, such as oil and gas, infrastructure, energy, or robotics.

A career goal can guide you into doing what you want with your engineering degree. It can help you prepare for your chosen career. It can let you know if you need additional experience, training, or certifications, such as an engineering license.

How do you determine which career path is correct for you, beyond the skills and educational requirements?

Consider your purpose, personality, and preferences. These things will increase your ability to make a great impression. When you like what you're doing, you'll have an easy time doing it.

How do you do it? Well, start by asking yourself what you value the most. Let's say environmental issues are important to you. You can specialize in energy, recycling, or electric vehicles. Or, let's say you value the idea of helping others. It might make sense to focus on prosthetics or wheelchairs. If you are like me, you're drawn to designing and developing processes that create products. Engineers are problem solvers. Which problems will *you* solve?

Career happiness doesn't depend on pay, amazing co-workers, or whether or not the boss is a wet blanket. It has more to do with whether your career matches your purpose.

Ask yourself these questions:

- What problems would I like to solve?
- What do I need to get started?
- How do I define my career success?

Read through the table on the next page. It is a sample of an ASCE (American Society of Civil Engineers) brochure that defines the general responsibilities and credentials of a recent engineering graduate through the first year. Consider using this information to plot your career goals for *your* first year.

Experience	0+ Years	1+ Years
Education	Bachelor's Degree ABET Accredited Program	Bachelor's Degree ABET Accredited Program
Licensure and Certification	Engineer-in-Training	Engineer-in-Training
General	Acquires limited knowledge and develops basic skills. Applies techniques and procedures to assigned tasks. Performs routine technical work that requires no experience. Acquires an understanding of professional and ethical responsibilities.	Acquires basic knowledge and develops skills in practice. Applies standard techniques, procedures, and criteria to perform assigned tasks as part of a broader assignment. Exercises limited judgment on details of work and in the application of standard methods for conventional work.

Experience	0+ Years	1+ Years
Technical Responsibilities	Collects data and gathers information or documents. Performs standard analysis. Prepares drawings and or visual aids. Observes construction activities.	Performs basic design tasks. Assists on other tasks, such as preparation of permit applications, material testing, drawings, specifications, and CAD design.
Managerial Responsibilities	None	Assigns tasks and coordinates with technicians and staff.
Direction Received	Close supervision on all assignments.	Close supervision on unusual assignments or difficult problems, general review, or all aspects of work.
Communication Skills	Basic oral and written. Interacts with staff.	Interacts with staff, public, officials, and contractors.
Typical Titles	Engineer-in-Training Engineering Intern Junior Engineer Staff Engineer	Engineer-in-Training Engineering Intern Junior Engineer Staff Engineer
Activities	Member of a professional organization, outreach, or community service.	Member of a professional organization, outreach, or community service.

(ASCE, 2019)

Below is a sample engineering student career plan. Your plan certainly does not have to match the one below, but it is essential to create your own. Notice I only listed goals for the next 4 years. Having a 20-year plan early on in your career is terrific, but not necessary. For now, decide what you want to do in the next couple of years and adjust in the future.

6 months	1 year	2 years	4 years
Graduate with a B.S. in Engineering	Increase my responsibilities	Complete my own designs	Pass the P.E. exam
Land an entry-level position	Member of a professional organization	Manage my own designs	
Pass the E.I.T exam	Learn a particular skill		

What is your plan?

6 months	1 year	2 years	4 years

"If plan A fails, remember there are 25 more letters!"
–Claire Cook

Before you start your job search journey, you must understand you are up against a lot of competition. There are many more engineers and job seekers out there searching for the same jobs you are. Remember, it is not the most qualified person who gets hired faster, but the person who is qualified and is in the right place, at the right time. You must create and follow a plan.

Imagine you're on your way to a suburban destination and following a map to get there. It is exciting to start your job search or start sending out résumés, but you have to be careful not to get ahead of yourself. Without a job search plan and a well-defined set of goals, you could end up moving in the wrong direction, and ending up somewhere further from your ultimate destination and true desires. A job search roadmap is critical. Without it, you can't be sure whether or not you're moving in the right direction! There's no point in landing a good job at a bad company. The more control you have over your job search journey, the better you'll feel and the better your job search results will be. Before you start your job search journey, remember that preparation is the first half of the battle.

Nader Mowlaee – Engineering Job Search Coach

Advanced Degrees

One question that I get asked constantly is whether or not a master's degree is worthwhile.

- It comes down to a few key issues:
- Do you want to teach?
- Do you want to do research?
- Is it a personal goal?

If you answer yes to any of these questions, you may want to continue your education by getting a master's degree or even a Ph.D. However, I strongly suggest working in the field for a year or two before getting an advanced degree. Experience enables you to contribute in higher ways. A teacher who has no experience isn't worth as much as one that does.

Even if you want to be involved in the business side of engineering, you don't necessarily need that graduate degree. An MBA is an opportunity to gain business management skills, but not a "license" to do business. Consider gaining experience first and determining what credentials you need to climb the ladder. An MBA is great, but only when it matches an opportunity and you have the requisite experience.

Credentials

The best advice I can give to a young engineer is to pass the Fundamentals of Engineering (F.E.) exam. It's easier than ever, flexible to your schedule, and a cost-effective way to accelerate your career.

The F.E. exam is focused on a wide variety of concepts learned in your university experience. It is much easier to pass this exam while you are in or recently out of school. Taking the test five years down the road is extremely difficult because you have likely forgotten subjects that you don't often use, such as chemistry, heat transfer, or thermodynamics. Don't trap yourself by skipping the exam and then hitting a glass ceiling down the road. It is okay to pass your F.E. exam and then never get your license, but it's challenging to approach that hurdle years later.

What if you are not planning on becoming a licensed engineer? Do you need to take the exam? No—but whether you want to get a license or not doesn't matter. The F.E. exam can provide many benefits to an entry-level engineer. It says to an employer, "I have the technical capability, and I am interested in taking my career to the next level." And besides—the letters E.I.T. after your name look great on a résumé.

Consider a Coach

"I absolutely believe that people, unless coached,
never reach their maximum potential."
—Bob Nardelli

Many professionals, at all levels, have used a professional coach. As you are launching your career, a coach can help. And while the excitement for a new job wears off over time, the relationship with the right coach can keep you engaged, challenged, and on the fast-track to success over the long haul.

What is necessary for a young engineer to successfully work with a coach to solve problems?

- A willingness to grow
- A gap between where you are (or are not) now and where you want to be
- With a coach, you will:
- Take more, better, and smarter action. You set the goals you want to attain.
- Coaching can help you have a balanced life, because you design it yourself, with professional guidance.
- A coach helps you to reach for more—much more—and not be consumed by the process.
- You will make better decisions for yourself and your career because your focus will be clear.

Finding the Right Coach

Navigating your professional career on your own is difficult. An excellent career coach can save you countless hours of frustration by sharing their experience and tips. A great career coach can also accelerate your progress faster and further. How do you find one?

Look for real evidence that a coach is invested in moving your career forward. Does the coach have at least a few years of experience? In the past, you would meet with a coach face-to-face or with a phone call to determine their level of expertise. These days, with social media, you have another tool. Coaching professionals create content, including websites, social media, blogging, podcasting, YouTube, and more. Check out a potential coach's paper trail. Do you relate to this person's personality? Is their content focused on your goals? Does this coach inspire you?

It's important to find a great coach, and part of that process is to find someone who has achieved success in the areas in which you would like to excel. For instance, an engineering coach would be great, but if you are looking to move up in management, an experienced engineering manager would be more beneficial.

A coach is not forever. As you grow, your challenges and goals will evolve. Today, you may be searching for your true purpose or starting your career. Down the road, your goal may be sales. Different coaches are suited for different phases of your life.

When I graduated from college with an engineering degree, it only took about a month in my new job for me to realize that I didn't know much about the real world of manufacturing. I had no purpose, I had no career plan, and I had few skills to contribute to my new job. I had college loans to pay, and it was scary right from the start.

But it got worse. Within six months, the manager of thermal processes (high-temperature kilns and dryers) left his position, and I was nominated to take his place. The kilns operated 24/7, and suddenly everyone in production and quality looked to me to solve problems, and I knew nothing about the system. So here's what I did:

I asked everyone connected to the output of thermal systems what problems they had. I looked for people who had practical knowledge more than those with theoretical knowledge. "Old timers" were full of experience, even though their theoretical knowledge was limited. At this point in my career, I needed quick solutions, and not theory.

I went to the university library and tried to find books on kilns…but there wasn't anything that seemed to answer my questions.

I started to develop my theories and studied literature on fluid flow. I read anything and everything that was even remotely related to my job responsibilities. I called combustion vendors and asked them lots of questions.

I worked 60-70 hours a week studying all of the quality data and relating it to process variability in my area.

I got lucky. Not only did I begin to understand the operation of 35 different firing systems, I realized that I liked the practical and theoretical aspects of this field. In fact, after around four years, I decided to make kiln and combustion design my career. It soon became apparent that to learn more; I had to leave industrial manufacturing and find a job in kiln and dryer design so that I could learn from experts. So that's what I did, and it started me on a path to become as proficient as I possibly could in my field.

During my interview with a first class manufacturer of kilns, I listened to and answered their questions. But then, I had the chance to tell them about my first job, and my passion (real, not contrived) became apparent, and they hired me on the spot. So my career path became clear—at least to me—and over a 45-year career, I ended up working for a total of 6 companies, all associated with my favorite engineering niche—kilns and their operation. I took a break from working for a company and opened my own consulting business, which was great fun. I traveled all over the world—45 weeks annually for 15 years—in that capacity and continued to learn about global design ideas (both good ones and bad ones!). And then one of my clients hired me to be president of their company, and I ended my professional career as president of a company that designed the best quality kilns.

My best guidance for those at the beginning of their career:

Work hard to become proficient in your responsibilities.

Ask lots of questions, not only of managers but also of workers who produce the product. Don't be afraid of the dumb question.

Put lots of time into finding something that you enjoy. If you love it, it will be easy. If you hate the job, assignments become more difficult. Find something else as quickly as you can.

Be kind to all people you meet. Not only is it easy to be nice, but more than half of those people will remember you when they grow and move into other positions or careers; they will think of you when an opportunity arises.

Help other people excel, and they will help you solve problems

Ralph Ruark – Director at Swindell International Co.

Chapter 3—What You Learned

In Chapter 3 we discussed how a great plan and a coach could help your chances of being successful. You now have a tool to set your short-term goals and keep track of your progress. Your plan is key to reaching your goals. Take it seriously and keep at it.

Action Items:

- Review the requirements of an entry-level engineer and complete the goal-setting table.
- Identify any credentials that you need to reach those goals.
- Do some research on coaching. It's very beneficial.
- You're doing well! Keep it up!

4

Identify What Employers Want

"One man's magic is another man's engineering. Supernatural is a null word."
–Robert A. Heinlein

Qualities That Employers Need

I surveyed hundreds of professionals that hire engineers and asked, "What are the qualities you are looking for?" Here is what they had to say:

Self-confidence – Fearless in asking questions, poised, and have a little grit.

Self-knowledge – Knows what he or she wants to do and demonstrates a specific interest in the job.

Self-driven – Passion for the job, and willing to do what needs to be done.

A positive attitude – Ready to take on any challenge.

Genuinely strives for excellence – Dedication to getting the work done while paying attention to detail.

Strong communication skills – Both oral and written.

Team oriented – Skills and tolerance to help resolve team conflicts.

Leadership – Ability to influence and lead.

Situational flexibility – Ability to quickly react and adapt to change; quick decision-making and problem-solving skills.

Trainability – Willingness and desire to learn.

Hard and Soft Skills

Hard skills stay the same regardless of which company, circumstance, or people you work with; soft skills, on the other hand, will change, depending on the company culture and people you work with. For example, calculations are a hard skill. The rules for mathematics are the same no matter where you work. Communication skills are a set of soft skills. The goal is to be clear, concise, and logical.

What's the difference between hard and soft skills? How do they apply to your career?

Hard Skills

Rules stay the same:

- Programming
- Math
- Physics

- Chemistry
- Statistics
- Writing

Soft Skills

Rules change:

- Communications
- Networking
- Leadership

- Confidence
- Self-management
- Public Speaking

Engineers need hard skills, but great engineers use both hard and soft skills. You need to understand the principles of science and accurately portray difficult principles and concepts; the future of your career depends on it. But engineers that achieve greatness do so because they have exceptional soft skills.

"In hiring recent college graduates, Jennifer Floren, founder and former CEO of Experience, Inc. noted: "Of all the things employers look for when hiring entry-level talent, it's the so-called 'soft skills' that are valued most: communication, teamwork, flexibility, and positive attitude are by far the most sought-after skills. Employers understand that everything else can be taught, so they look for the most promising raw material to work with."
(Ricci, 2012)

As an engineer, you are expected to understand and apply the engineering skills for which you are being paid. Stay focused, be diligent and do a great job. Come up for air too! One personal character trait you should strive for that sums it all up is integrity. It's acquired over time. Get started.

Tom Glassbrenner – Founder Ventilations Systems, LLC

Attitudes Employers Want

Each one of us defines career success differently. Most of us want to spend less time at work, but if we have to be there, we want to enjoy what we are doing. Life is too short for a career that we hate. Here are my best tips on how you can achieve success in your career:

Increase personal awareness – Awareness is an important key to personal improvement. By being aware of your strengths and weaknesses, you can adapt your career accordingly. You can also appropriately add to your own growth and knowledge. Could you tolerate sitting eight to twelve hours in an office working on a computer? Would you rather work with your hands in the field, testing, or doing experiments? No matter your strengths or weaknesses, you should use them to your advantage.

Assume responsibility – What's the difference between mediocre and successful engineers? Responsibility. While you may not apply it every day, the concept is familiar. Assume responsibility for all of your actions and never blame others for your mistakes. Do not take things personally, and remain calm.

Raise your standards – Your standards impact the way you think, believe, and behave. If your standards are high, you'll never be satisfied with less than you can accomplish. What are your rules for things like calculations, drawings, or specifications? If they are average, you will never get better. Engineers with high standards achieve more.

Root for yourself – If you aren't your biggest fan, no one else will be. Take notes on your successes and accomplishments; don't wait for anyone else to acknowledge them. Reflecting and documenting your achievements will help you accomplish better ones and can keep your head up in difficult times. Documenting will help you have material for future résumés or to "sell" yourself.

Measure your success – How do you measure your success? The size of your paycheck or office? Do you desire a sense of accomplishment from your designs? Perhaps you like the thought of leaving the office at 4 pm and not thinking about your daily duties. You are the only person that can determine what success means to you. Define your success!

Ask for help – No one can have all the knowledge and insight needed to excel in every area. It's unwise to rely solely on your own abilities and experience.

For example, five years after I graduated, I ran into a huge potential issue. My task was to design a lifting system for a furnace; I had completed the design and my boss was now reviewing it.

"Tom, did you check the critical speed of these shafts?"

"Ummm…what?" I said.

"The critical speeds, did you check them?"

"No, sir."

I had no idea what he was asking me. I pulled out my machinery notes from college and started looking through the lecture. I found what I needed on two pages of notes out of 800. The topic was probably covered in 10 minutes of a 3-hour lecture that occurred five years before.

It turns out that the critical speed of shafts is an essential calculation to determine the velocities at which drive shafts reach a harmonic range and vibrate themselves to failure. *Crap!*

So…my suggestion is to ask for help regularly, even if you believe your work is correct. If my boss had not grabbed my design and asked the question, I would have had a mess on my hands. There is never a situation in engineering where the question "Can you double check this for me?" is inappropriate.

Own your mistakes – You will make mistakes. Engineers who claim they don't make mistakes have never worked outside of their comfort zones. What you do after you make a mistake is the difference between a great engineer and a bad one. Admit your error, find a way to fix it, and use it as a learning experience. This will help shift your reputation from someone that makes mistakes to a go-getter.

Lose the negative attitude – Don't be a curmudgeon. Don't wallow in misery and ask yourself why things are so bad. They aren't. Some people see only the negative side and always have a complaint.

For example, years ago, I was traveling with an engineer who hated the beautiful hotel where we were staying. When I asked him why, he said, "They don't give free newspapers. They're digital." Don't be that person. Look on the brighter side and avoid those with negative attitudes. Maintaining a positive attitude will help you and others around you. With people and relationships, you get what you put in. Kindness and positivity will allow you to gain cooperation and friendship.

Listen closely – You will learn more if you are an active listener, and gain nothing if you aren't. Whether you are in a sales meeting or listening to co-workers talk about their weekend, seek to truly understand what others are or are not saying. It will help you build rapport.

Become a fighter – Not physically, of course. Be resilient. It's a necessary attribute on the way to achievement. Don't let the smallest of issues turn into larger ones. Often, I see young engineers overcome with failure over the most trivial problem. Suck it up and move on. Let the issues slide off your shoulders, and keep your head up.

Communication Skills

"Communication is a skill that you can learn. It is like riding a bicycle or typing. If you're willing to work at it, you can rapidly improve the quality of every part of your life."
–Brian Tracy

Do you remember the telephone game? In school, you and your classmates pick a phrase and "pass it on" by whispering it to the person next to you. The phrase travels from person to person until the last person announces what they heard. How much does the phrase change during the game? As people relay messages from one person to the other, it often gets distorted.

While the game is a lot of fun, it teaches us valuable lessons.

If you do not receive information from a reliable source, you may not get the correct information. It turns into gossip. If you do not produce information correctly, it will not be received as planned. Communication skills are vital to success in your personal life and your career. A poorly delivered message can turn into a misunderstanding, an exercise in frustration, or even an accident.

By practicing your communication skills, you will understand more of what people say. Your family, friends, and co-workers will have the confidence to come to you when they find themselves in need. What are the keys to clear communication?

Listening – A key to verbal communication is truly listening, not just waiting to speak. To actively listen to someone, make mental notes of key points when someone is talking to you. Deciding what to say must come second to understanding. When you have a chance to speak, you can respond to the most vital issues. When others are speaking, focus on the exact words they are saying. This will help you comprehend more information and have a more successful conversation.

Are you confused? Repeat what you think the speaker said and ask if that is correct. This inspires the speaker to clarify his or her needs, which will help you to understand.

Proper speech – Be clear and concise. Speak on important matters directly and try to keep the listeners' attention. Make sure that you are certain the listener understands your points and explain further if necessary. Do not expect someone to "know" what you are saying. Don't assume.

Consistent communication – Great leaders practice the skill of consistent communication. Each one of us has a different approach to portraying a vision. Find your voice—and then practice. Your approach will help your audience comprehend your information more efficiently. Using consistent communication can also make your tone more successful.

Patience – During interactions, give others time to communicate. Stay focused on what they are trying to say, and stay open to assisting with their issues. Communication lines tend to break down when impatience gets in the way of the conversation. Every conversation you are involved in is essential!

Practicing communication skills – Consider Toastmasters International™, a non-profit organization focused on communication and leadership development. The organization has more than 357,000 members who improve their speaking and leadership skills by attending one of the 16,600 clubs in 143 countries. Members are encouraged to practice their leadership and communication skills by regularly giving speeches, receiving feedback, leading teams, and guiding others to achieve their goals in a supportive atmosphere. Not only is Toastmasters™ fun, but it's also great to put on a résumé! To learn more, visit www.toastmasters.org.

> **Engage the Audience: What's in it for Them (WIIFT)?**
>
> Have you ever found yourself speaking in front of a group of people and wondering, *are they paying any attention at all?*
>
> It's probably happened to all of us at some point. We've been asked to speak at a meeting, give a presentation, make a pitch, or deliver a speech. We prepare and rehearse and plan – only to be met with blank looks and bored faces. One way to combat low engagement and energy is to get the audience involved.

A trap that many of us fall into when asked to speak is thinking about the experience from only our perspective. What am I trying to accomplish? What do I need to say, teach, or explain? What do I want the group to think or feel or do after they hear me?

While these are all important considerations, the crucial question we need to answer is: **What's in it for them?**

When you're trying to persuade, inspire or educate a group, think of the experience as more of a conversation with the audience than a lecture at them. Put yourself in their shoes and figure out what they care about or what they want to know.

Once you answer the question of how your material is relevant to them, you can decide how you'll encourage them to participate. Will you:

- Ask questions and encourage the audience to answer?
- Tell stories to illustrate your points?
- Use visuals that enhance (not act as) your content?
- Solicit audience feedback?
- Use technology that allows the audience to respond to in-the-moment polls and surveys?
- Incorporate real-time feedback via social media?
- Facilitate an activity or exercise that lets them experience firsthand the point you're trying to get across?

Some situations lend themselves more easily to engaging the audience than others. A group of colleagues meeting to discuss a project is a very different audience from conference workshop attendees or investors at a pitch meeting.

You'll need to tailor how you engage the audience to the circumstances. Consider the size of the group, the way the room is configured, and how much time you have. For example, having participants complete an activity in small groups is much easier in a room where they're seated at round tables than in an auditorium with seats bolted to the floor.

Whatever the logistics are, answering "WIIFT?" can help you create a powerful, engaging connection with the group. Draw them out, encourage their participation, and speak to their concerns, needs, and hopes. They'll appreciate your approach – and you'll have a more rewarding experience, too.

Kathi Finch – Founder, Finch Communications

Chapter 4—What You Learned

In Chapter 4, we discussed the difference between hard and soft skills and what type of qualities employers need. Recognizing these essential traits can help you to realize where you are competent and where you need to put in some work.

Action Items:

- Write down your three best skills and three best qualities; these are important to selling yourself on your résumé and in person.
- Write down three skills you need to address. Consider communication—it's often underrated and overlooked.
- Attend a Toastmasters™ meeting. Take a look at the website and discover clubs in your area. Attendance is free, and the people you will meet will be warm and friendly.

5

Craft an Excellent Résumé

"If you call failures experiments, you can put them in your résumé and claim them as achievements."
—Mason Cooley

Your résumé is how you say, "I'm great at this; I've achieved that, and this is how I can help your company." That is why you should create an impressive, professional, concise, and visually appealing résumé. Opportunities are everywhere. Be ready with an extraordinary résumé.

When employers and recruiters want to fill a position, they can obtain dozens of résumés in no time. They spend as little as fifteen—often less than five—seconds on a résumé before deciding which candidates are worth pursuing. Initial candidates will be chosen or rejected solely on their résumés. You must catch an employer's attention with your résumé to be able to land an interview.

Sell your skills and accomplishments in your résumé. Selling yourself may sound illegal, but it's all about your sales pitch. You are selling your knowledge and capabilities. It's not about what you have done—it's about selling what you can do for the employer. How can you help them?

Have you ever seen *The Wolf of Wall Street*? In the movie, Jordan Belfort asks an audience member a firm request: "Sell me this pen." The reply he receives does not please him. So he asks another. Both dissatisfy him. The truth is, it's a trick question.

Our instinct is to sell the features of the pen before we know the buyer. If the pen is blue, why try and sell the blue feature? Maybe the buyer hates blue. Perhaps he or she prefers the pen for the gel instead of ink. We all have different needs and wants. Don't assume the buyer likes the same features as you do. Remember, it's about the buyer, and the benefits that the pen's features provide them.

Young engineers have a difficult time articulating what exactly they can do for employers. Part of the issue is that most only have a vague idea about the business of engineering and have been performing mostly calculations for the extent of their education. Set yourself apart. Tell the employer what makes you different. Explain how you can help prospective employers on your résumé.

It is essential to know yourself. If you have achieved something, say it. Put yourself in the best light. Avoid subjective statements such as "I am a hard worker," or "I get along well with my co-workers." Use the facts. Don't be modest, but don't exaggerate your achievements to the point of misrepresentation. Most companies will immediately drop an applicant from consideration upon discovering inaccurate information on a résumé.

Add the important things you have done, but do it as concisely as possible. An entry-level engineering résumé should highlight your collegiate training. Be sure to list qualifiers like internships, volunteer experiences, or part-time jobs that you have held while you were in school or after you graduated.

Your résumé will be scanned, not read, and short phrases are much more effective than long sentences. Avoid the use of "I" when stressing your accomplishments. Instead, use short phrases beginning with action verbs.

Some technical terms will be unavoidable, but try to avoid excessive technical terminology. An HR manager may be the first person to see your résumé, and that person may not necessarily know the jargon. It's hard for them to be impressed by something incomprehensible.

Keep your paragraphs to six lines or less. If you have more than six lines of information about one job or school, put it in two or more sections.

Take time with the appearance of your résumé. Before reading your résumé, a hiring manager or recruiter will begin to form an opinion of it—and you—based on the format. A résumé that is long, poorly organized, or difficult to read will have little chance of landing you an interview.

For a sample résumé and step-by-step instructions, keep reading.

Résumé Outline

James T. Kirk

Pittsburgh, PA
(724) 555-0000
JamesTKirk@gmail.com
www.linkedin.com/in/James-T-Kirk

Summary

Mechanical Engineer with X years' experience designing and managing equipment.
James completes projects on time, on budget, that meet the customer's needs, and increases revenue. His technical knowledge can help your customers solve complex issues and processes. He has a strong sense of ownership, personal accountability, and works beyond his duties to improve products. Never satisfied with his own performance, he continually thinks of ways to improve designs, procurement, and execution. He is passionate about his career.

Areas of Expertise

Heat Transfer	Public Speaking	Project Management
Thermodynamics	Technical Specifications	Construction Management
Fluid Mechanics	Communication	Preventative Maintenance
Machine Design	Business Development	Commissioning
Process Control	Customer Relations	2D & 3D Drafting

Work History

Engineering Title   ***BUSINESS NAME.*** City, STATE.   YEAR - Present
Short, concise statement of your duties and your experience.
- Accomplishment 1
- Accomplishment 2
- Accomplishment 3
- Accomplishment 4

Engineering Title   ***BUSINESS NAME.*** City, STATE.   YEAR - YEAR
Short, concise statement of your duties and your experience.
- Accomplishment 1
- Accomplishment 2
- Accomplishment 3
- Accomplishment 4

Engineering Title   ***BUSINESS NAME.*** City, STATE.   YEAR - YEAR
Short, concise statement of your duties and your experience.
- Accomplishment 1
- Accomplishment 2
- Accomplishment 3
- Accomplishment 4

Education

Name of University   Bachelor of Applied Science   YEAR
Mechanical Engineering

Certifications, Awards, Organizations, Training

✓ Engineering Society	✓ EIT Certification	✓ OSHA 10 Certification
✓ Toastmasters	✓ ASME	✓ Student Government
✓ Skills Training	✓ ASCE	✓ Engineering Club

Contact Information

James T. Kirk

Pittsburgh, PA
(724) 555-0000
JamesTKirk@gmail.com
www.linkedin.com/in/James-T-Kirk

Your name, phone number, e-mail address, LinkedIn URL and location should be at the top of your résumé. Make your name stand out by using a slightly larger font size or all capital letters. Be sure to use designations like B.S., M.S., Ph.D., MBA, etc. if you have them. Be sure to spell out items like Street for St. and Road for Rd.

Whatever phone number you use, make sure it has an appropriate voicemail message. Loud music in the background, a joke message that your friends find hilarious, or a message that doesn't include your actual name may cause recruiters to reconsider their call.

Remember that employers will keep your résumé on file and may contact you months later if a position opens that fits your qualifications. All too often, candidates are unreachable because they have moved and did not provide enough contact options on their résumé. If you think you may be relocating within six months, include a second address and phone number of a trusted friend or relative.

Summary Section

Summary

Mechanical Engineer with X years' experience designing and managing equipment.
James completes projects on time, on budget, that meet the customer's needs, and increases revenue. His technical knowledge can help your customers solve complex issues and processes. He has a strong sense of ownership, personal accountability, and works beyond his duties to improve products. Never satisfied with his own performance, he continually thinks of ways to improve designs, procurement, and execution. He is passionate about his career.

What will attract a hiring manager to your résumé? Use a summary section to describe what makes you great for a position. It is one of the most critical factors in determining whether you get a call for an interview. It needs to be persuasive, concise, and present a well-rounded picture. Listed below are the items you must have in your summary:

- Relevant education, certification, or accomplishments
- Characteristics that make you a good fit for the company
- Skills you've demonstrated that are relevant to the position
- Experience that shows you're qualified for the position

Make sure your best factors are first and keep the summary brief. To get the hiring manager's attention, you should tailor your summary. When you customize it to a job posting, you are saying, "I hear you. You need a candidate with these qualities, and I have them." Use specifics where you can.

Use the job description to create your summary, and be sure to match the exact phrasing. For instance, if you are applying to a "project engineering" position, use that term instead of "entry level engineer" or "mechanical engineer." Here are two more sample summaries:

- Engineering graduate with leadership training and experience with academic training at the University of _____. Proven skills in project management, organization, and research. Able to provide employers with engineering support and professional communication skills.
- Organized, versatile and reliable _____ Engineering graduate with two years' experience. Excels in organization, communication, and problem-solving.

If you want to stand out from your competition, you can't do it by using edgy fonts and fancy résumé layouts. You must focus less on the design of your résumé and more on the content, context, storytelling, and relevancy. You will stand out by being the person who communicates better. You must tell clearer, concise stories relevant to the employer's pains and needs. Do this right, and you'll get more job interviews in much less time.

Nader Mowlaee – Job Search Coach for Engineers

Areas of Expertise / Skills

Areas of Expertise

Heat Transfer	Public Speaking	Project Management
Thermodynamics	Technical Specifications	Construction Management
Fluid Mechanics	Communication	Preventative Maintenance
Machine Design	Business Development	Commissioning
Process Control	Customer Relations	2D & 3D Drafting

List the skills and abilities that are relevant to the company and position you are applying for. This includes both hard and soft skills.

Hard skills may include word processing, programming, computation fluid dynamics, machine operation, AutoCAD, etc.

Soft skills may include problem-solving, communication, speaking, teamwork, time management, etc.

Work History

Work History

Engineering Title	***BUSINESS NAME.*** City, STATE.	YEAR - Present

Short, concise statement of your duties and your experience.
- Accomplishment 1
- Accomplishment 2
- Accomplishment 3
- Accomplishment 4

Engineering Title	***BUSINESS NAME.*** City, STATE.	YEAR - YEAR

Short, concise statement of your duties and your experience.
- Accomplishment 1
- Accomplishment 2
- Accomplishment 3
- Accomplishment 4

Engineering Title	***BUSINESS NAME.*** City, STATE.	YEAR - YEAR

Short, concise statement of your duties and your experience.
- Accomplishment 1
- Accomplishment 2
- Accomplishment 3
- Accomplishment 4

This section is also called "Relevant Experience" or "Work Experience." Include only paid work (full-time, part-time, self-employment, internships, etc.) Be sure not to leave out the following:

- Names of organizations where you were employed
- City and state of each organization
- Positions or titles you held
- Employment periods are written as Month/Date – Month/Date
- Brief description or a bullet list of responsibilities

One essential part of the work experience section is finding the best way to list your contributions to the company. Be accurate and concise. Start with the essential points and work down.

Not this:

Gained successful experience with flow control systems, check valve unseating, hydraulic & manual lubricators, field pressure testing, field service reporting, Drilling Systems planned preventative maintenance, casing hanging equipment, sealing technology, TSS, MNDS systems, MBS SWE. Conventional SWE, casing cutting, Christmas tree, surface wellhead equipment, torqueing operation, connectors, tubing/casing hanging equipment, pressure control equipment, frac tree systems, greasing, flowback systems, gate & ball valves, actuators, well testing, and measurement systems.

Much better:

Experienced with hydraulic, pressure and flow control, flowback, frac tree, and various measurement systems. Completed numerous field pressure tests, service reporting, well testing, and planned preventative maintenance.

Not this:

I worked on a daily basis with the company's most important clients helping them solve problems and making them happy.

Much better:

I worked daily with clients to solve problems.

Education

Education

Name of University	Bachelor of Applied Science	YEAR
	Mechanical Engineering	

In general, you should put the dates of your education, the degree, and school(s) you attended. The most important thing is to break up the text in some logical way that makes your résumé visually attractive and easy to scan. Long descriptions of the purpose of your degree or listing relevant coursework aren't necessary. Engineering managers know what your degree is all about.

Certifications, Awards, Organizations, Training

Certifications, Awards, Organizations, Training

✓ Engineering Society	✓ EIT Certification	✓ OSHA 10 Certification
✓ Toastmasters	✓ ASME	✓ Student Government
✓ Skills Training	✓ ASCE	✓ Engineering Club

Highlight important details like coursework, projects, and honors:

- Independent projects
- Internships
- Volunteer experiences
- Honors activities and awards
- Part-time employment
- Independent work experiences
- Student or part-time work awards and honors

Proofreading

Read your résumé backward. Mistakes are often much more apparent if you're not reading in the same order as you have before. Use a spell checker to double check for spelling errors; keep in mind that it will not find mistakes such as "to" for "two" or "wok" for "work."

- Proofread your document as carefully as possible to check for grammatical mistakes.
- Get a friend to proofread for you.
- Read your draft aloud.
- Have your friend read aloud while you check.

- Read the document letter by letter to check spelling and punctuation.

Let's eat grandma.

Let's eat, grandma.

Punctuation saves lives!

Résumé Dos and Don'ts

- Make sure your résumé gives an excellent first impression
- Correct inconsistencies in fonts, spacing, or tenses

Include personal info in the header:

- Full name
- Phone number
- Email
- Personal website or blog
- Custom LinkedIn URL

Format your résumé:

- One page max
- Print your résumé on 24 lb, high quality 8-1/2" x 11" paper
- Use a conservative color, such as white, ivory, or pale grey
- Test print your résumé and cover letter
- Use a font between 10- and 12-point, except for name and headings
- Use Courier or Helvetica font
- Boldface and all capital letters are best only for major section headings, such as "Experience" and "Education."

Items that absolutely should not be on your résumé:

- Borders or graphics
- A font smaller than 10

- A spritz of perfume or cologne
- Your picture
- A watermark or images in the background
- Handwriting your résumé or cover letter
- Every class you took in engineering school
- Job info that doesn't apply; your month at McDonald's doesn't belong
- Long descriptions of something simple

Résumé Terms

Worst Résumé Terms	Best Résumé Terms
Best of breed	Achieved
Go-getter	Lead
Think outside of the box	Improved
Synergy	Trained/Mentored
Go-to person	Managed
Results-driven	Created
Team player	Influenced
Hard worker	Increased/Decreased
Strategic thinker	Negotiated
Detail-oriented	Launched
Successful experience	Under budget
In my wheelhouse	On time

Action Verbs in Context

Applied knowledge of thermodynamics, reactor design, phase separation, fluid compression, expansion, and process control to complete simulations.

Provided engineering estimates and specifications for industrial, commercial, and power facilities.

Evaluated new product designs, solving environmental problems on prototypes.

Assisted engineers by working on load monitors, gauge weight and distribution properties on heavy machine presses.

Conducted a variety of tensile, compression, and creep tests on modeled parts.

Assembled machines from drawing specifications.

Observed and **participated** in the exploration of mines.

Repaired generators, electrical motors, and mechanical systems aboard rail units for public transport.

Prepared and **completed** residential building maintenance services.

Scheduled and **supervised** project work on a transportation model.

Oversaw work delegated to subcontractors for public sectors.

Served as an engineer on railroad signal, traffic signal, and wastewater teams.

Conducted accident statistical data analysis for warning and labeling issues.

Constructed sports facilities, railroads, bridges, and worked on building restorations.

Skilled in computer-aided design (CAD) layout for intricate building plans.

Experienced in roofing, window framing, tiling, siding, flooring, and renovation.

Managed architectural projects from conceptual design to completion.

Created and **interpreted** programs to evaluate and modify product performance.

Developed standard designs for retaining walls and reinforced-concrete bridge abutments.

Used verbal specifications to **develop** electronic illustrations for new and changed products.

Researched the effect of worldwide television deregulation on broadcast, cable and satellite television, as well as international broadcasting and advertising.

Obtained new accounts to replace lost business and maintain profitability.

Utilized sales expertise and account management to develop an eighty percent-new client base and maintain profit margins.

Administered and **directed** marketing activities of sales operations.

Organized and **planned** actions that impact various sectors of aluminum markets.

Worked with internal divisions and outside agencies to develop plans that supported company activities.

Planned and **supervised** training activities.

Organized a smoothly functioning administration and operational division.

Maintained detailed knowledge of all aspects to include maintenance, logistics, and communications.

(Rocha, 2005)

ATS Software

The Applicant Tracking System (or ATS software) is a software application that enables a company to process résumés electronically. ATS collects and stores candidate and job-related data. It also tracks and monitors candidates through all stages of the hiring process. In theory, these systems should save time by highlighting top candidates. In reality, ATS narrows the applicant pool, but top candidates may be eliminated. ATS is like a funnel for résumés: Most don't make it out the other end.

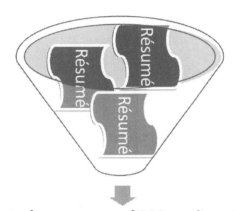

Out of an average of 200 applicants, 2-4 will get chosen for an interview. That's a 3% chance you'll get picked.

Generally, ATS is used for larger companies and recruiters. If you apply for a job online, your résumé may not go directly to a recruiter or hiring manager; ATS may process it. Whether a human ever sees your résumé depends on how well your résumé works with the software's algorithms.

If you're applying online, you'll face an ATS. Even job sites like Indeed and LinkedIn have their own built-in ATS. Jobscan research found that ninety eight percent of Fortune 500 companies use ATS. A Kelly OCG survey estimated sixty six percent of large companies and thirty five percent of small organizations use ATS. (Shields, 2018)

So, how do you beat ATS?

- Use standard résumé headings like "summary," "career summary," and "work experience."

- Choose a standard résumé format. Use a standard chronological form and make sure your résumé is formatted correctly and simply.

- Stay simple. Colors, images, and tables, although eye-catching, will confuse ATS.

- Predict and add the proper keywords to your résumé based on the job description. If you can predict the appropriate keywords, you will have the greatest chance of being included in the search results.

- Leave the headers and footers empty.

- Use standard 1" margins and left alignment.

- Write out all of your acronyms.

- Use a conservative font like Courier or Helvetica.

- Use a .docx or .pdf file format.

Remember, keep your formatting as simple as possible. Make your headings simple, use consistent formatting for dates, and avoid tables.

The best way?

Consider avoiding ATS altogether. Stop applying online. Stop competing with hundreds of other engineers for the same lousy position you may not even want anyway.

Network. Get yourself out there and find a job that suits you. Using connections, you can move your résumé to the top of the pile or even find an unadvertised job. If you get yourself out there and convince hiring managers that you can be a great asset to their organization, you can leave your competition in the dust.

If you are intimidated by networking or don't know how to go about it, don't worry. I'll discuss networking in detail in the next chapter.

> Now, this goes without saying, but I see it happen daily. Did you know that over 50% of the résumés we review at Storeyline Résumés have mistakes on them? Sad, but true. Now, you would think that with all the talk about the "perfect" résumé, that this would be something that people would pay closer attention to, but day in and day out, I see some very wacky, albeit funny typos on résumés.
>
> **Robynn Storey**, PHR – Storeyline Résumés

Chapter 5—What You Learned

Now you have a great résumé. I mean it. If you have followed this chapter, you have put together a winning résumé that you can use to land the job of your dreams. But remember, the résumé isn't everything. Often young engineers believe that the résumé is ninety percent of the work it takes to land your best job. In reality, it's more like ten percent. It's now time to reach out and land some fantastic opportunities.

Action Items:

- How is your résumé? Give it a grade from 1-10. If you are an 8, it's time to move on. If you are at a 7 or below, ask for others to help you.

- Use the dos and don'ts as a checklist. If you have worked through this list already, do it again.

- Proofread. Consider reading your résumé backward and asking those around you for help.

6

Get Networking

"Your network is the people who want to help you, and you want to help them, and that's really powerful."
–Reid Hoffman

What Does It Take?

In my conversations with young engineers, one question prevails over the rest: "I've filled out hundreds of online applications, and I have only gotten a few responses. How do I land my first engineering job?" It's too common. Young engineers often do not know how to obtain contacts in the engineering industry. So how do you do it? It starts with networking.

Networking

Networking can be intimidating—and to some, debilitating. It doesn't matter whether you're an introvert or extrovert. It is challenging to put yourself out there and be vulnerable in an uncomfortable space. Networking is hoping for the best and generally expecting the worst. Networking, however, is necessary to land and create an excellent career. According to Hubspot:

- 85% of jobs are landed by networking.
- One out of four jobseekers don't network at all.
- 41% of networkers want to do so more frequently, but don't have enough time.
- 68% of entry-level professionals find face-to-face networking more valuable than online.
- Only 11% of LinkedIn users have more than 100 people in their network.

(Frost, 2017)

The numbers say it all. Eighty five percent of jobs are filled through networking! This has also been true in my career. Every job I have landed has been through my contacts and networking.

It pays to be uncomfortable. You learn from the experiences that frighten you, and over time, networking gets easier. You gain a routine that helps you feel comfortable. It allows you to shine during networking events and limits second-guessing.

Networking, at its core, is relationship building. You send yourself off to make friends just as your parents did years ago. You are creating a mutually beneficial connection. Sounds a lot like selling, right? Many of the skills you need to build and maintain a network are the same ones you use to sell a product or service. So, it's also an excellent opportunity to work on your sales skills. Here are some tips that have helped me to overcome my networking fears.

Networking events and conferences can be intimidating. Try to start small. Start by networking on LinkedIn. Try to connect with someone new by sending him or her a note. Introduce yourself and tell the person why you're sending a message…and why you're worth a response.

Example: *Hi, I'm _____. I'm a _____ engineer, and I'm curious how you landed your position at your current company? How you selected a career path?*

At networking events, a friend can provide you the comfort you need to get over the networking jitters…but don't spend the whole time talking to your friend. Give yourselves 30 minutes to become acquainted with the area and guests, and then separate. Make it a point to meet others for a while. Spend that time mixing and mingling. When the event slows down, or you run out of people to talk to, find your friend again.

Make personal business cards, whether you are employed or not. Why? How are you going to easily exchange contact information without them? They are so much fun to make, and cost as little as $10. Include your name, email, phone number, website or social media, and a phrase for people to remember who you are. Better yet, add a professional photo, or they may forget your beautiful face. A picture makes a significant difference when someone is sorting through numerous business cards.

"You never get a second chance to make a first impression."
—Will Rogers

Your local chamber of commerce is a great place to meet local business leaders. Organizations like these are designed to promote business networking. Industry conventions are also a great place to meet and greet potential contacts. Every attendee is a potential hiring manager—or at least someone who knows one in your field.

When networking, don't let the conversation center on you. This is not always easy when you are excited about the discussion. Ask questions to get to know the other person. Starting a dialogue that fosters a relationship is much better than merely presenting yourself. Asking questions makes you more memorable because people love to talk about themselves.

Make it a goal to be open, friendly, and honest to everyone you meet, not only those in your field. Kindness is an attractive quality, and it's something people will remember about you.

Try to discover the value in each person you meet. Ask questions and listen—*really* listen. Don't make the mistake of pulling out your phone. Remember, you are providing value to each other. Push yourself to make some lasting connections. Make the event worth your while.

When you meet someone who is a great mutual connection, go beyond exchanging business cards and determine who is going to reach out and how. Make sure to agree to another interaction. It can be a phone call, email, LinkedIn contact, meeting, or whatever you choose. Make sure to agree to the next step before parting ways to avoid missing an opportunity.

Follow through. You don't want all that effort in your networking event to go to waste. Even if you left a great first impression, if you don't keep your commitments, you will seem unreliable and spoil the impression you are trying to make.

Now that you are clear on networking basics, principles, and the right mindset, *get out there*. Put yourself on the line to engage with those who can help your career, and others whose career you may be able to help. Who knows who you may end up meeting and what impact they can have on your life? What kind of networking does it take to land a job? Contact with seventy-five hiring managers. Start small and be diligent.

"I'm quitting," my coworker and structural engineer, Ann, announced to me one day over lunch.

I looked at Ann in surprise. I had started at this firm about a year before her. Both of us only had about two years' experience in our field, and the economy was coming out of an economic downturn.

"I'm sorry to see you go," I said. "Can you tell me where you're going and when we'll have to say goodbye?"

Ann proceeds to tell me that a friend of a friend had contacted her for a new position. The new position paid significantly more, allowed her to work from home some of the time, allowed her to travel occasionally, and gave her more autonomy over her work. Two years out of school, and she'd been offered an awesome job she couldn't turn down, all without actively looking for a job.

Was Ann a smarter or better engineer than I? Nope (at least in my humble opinion). The only difference between Ann and me was that she was much better connected than me. She knew how to network, and it got her a dream job.

Stephanie Slocum, P.E. – Founder, Engineers Rising LLC and author of the book *She Engineers*.

Have a Nice Conversation

Making conversation can be difficult, especially if you are an introvert, or have nothing in common with the person you're trying to talk to. Learning to have nice conversations can become more comfortable if you practice.

Timing is key – People do not like to be interrupted—so instead of just stopping by to have a private conversation with your boss, try asking, "Are you free to chat tomorrow?" Scheduling time in advance will ensure that you both have uninterrupted time for a productive conversation. Plus, he or she will probably ask what it's about. Letting your boss know the subject beforehand will allow them time to prepare.

If you make eye contact with someone, it may be time for a conversation. For instance, if you're in a grocery store and someone is looking at the same product as you, you could say "This looks tasty," or "Have you tried this?"

Comment on your surroundings – Spark a conversation by commenting on your surroundings. A spur of the moment conversation is a great way to practice your skills. Try asking "How's the coffee?" or stating, "What a nice place." Do your best to make it completely natural. Keep a positive attitude.

Remember names – This can make it much easier to make a connection and have a second conversation, but it can be difficult. When you learn someone's name, repeat it. When someone says, "Hi, I'm Earl," you should say, "It's nice to meet you, Earl." The immediate repetition will help you imprint the name in your memory.

Offer a compliment – Choose something specific to compliment. Be sincere. Your tone and facial expressions will reveal your sincerity. Try saying something encouraging. "I enjoyed that presentation yesterday. Could you give me tips on PowerPoint?" It starts the conversation on a positive note and opens the door for more discussions.

Selling Yourself

Why do engineers need to know how to sell? Sure, there are positions— Sales Engineers, for example—that exist to sell products or services, but they aren't the only engineers who need to know how to sell. You need to have sales skills for many reasons: When looking for a job, asking for a raise, applying for a promotion, convincing customers about designs, or convincing others to choose a particular solution. The selling of ideas and solutions is an integral part of every engineer's career.

Regardless of your industry, the sales tactics below can help you improve how you sell yourself, your ideas, and your products to anyone.

Define your buyer – Whether you are an equipment designer, consultant, sales engineer or job seeker, you'll have much more success if you're accustomed to the characteristics of your target buyers, and thoroughly qualify each prospect against an ideal buyer or job opportunity. By finding ideal buyers, you can save time and money by avoiding dead or poor leads. You will allow yourself more time to devote to ideal customers.

Do your research – If you expect buyers to spend time to learn about you, your product, or a solution, you need to spend time learning about them first. There's no excuse to call or send an email to a buyer, customer, or potential employer without knowledge of what they do and what matters to them. Sell yourself.

Here are eight places to research buyers before you attempt to engage in conversation:

- LinkedIn
- Twitter
- Company's website
- Company's news releases
- Blogs
- Company financial information
- Facebook
- Google

Build rapport first – During a networking event, you certainly don't ask, "Do you have a job for me?" It's best to start by saying, "Hello," and

"Have you been to this event before?" You might sprinkle in a comment like, "Nice weather today," or questions like, "What brings you here?"

If you notice someone you'd like to talk to lives in Cleveland (poor guy), talk about any experiences you have with Cleveland. Get to know the hiring manager before asking for a job or work. The relationship you form is key to landing a position.

Contribute…then sell yourself – When talking to a potential hiring manager, don't jump right in with your pitch—you run the risk of annoying them. Instead, offer them ways you can help. Not sure where you can help? Ask. As a social selling expert, Jill Rowley puts it, "Think 'jab, jab, jab, right hook' as 'give, give, give, and then ask.'"

Make it about them – Just like you hate listening to someone ramble about nothing, people dislike hearing you talk at length about something they don't care about. What you perceive as informative and exciting may be irrelevant and even obnoxious to them.

Make the conversation about them. When interviewing, tell the employer how you will help their business. When asking for a promotion, tell your boss how the promotion will help the company. Everything you try to sell should be about the buyer, not about you.

Pay attention to their personality. Do they possess strong analytical skills? Do they have an expressive personality?

Following are four main personality types:

Assertive/Director – Interested in results and the bottom line. Often demanding. Concerned with facts, not small talk. Compliment their decisiveness, let them make their own decisions, and never tell them they are wrong.

Sociable – Outgoing, enjoy chatting and making new friends. Interested in creative ideas and big-picture visions. Wants a relationship with you and to like you. Compliment them. Remember the names of the people around them. Interact with them consistently and be as friendly as possible.

Relator – Needs to be part of a group. Takes ownership in everything they do. Interested in people and how ideas affect others. Ask their opinions and include them in as much of the process as possible.

Analytics – Interested in facts, figures, accuracy, and analysis. Information motivated. Give details and fact; avoid useless statements. Ask their opinions and support them with relevant facts.

Once you know who you are selling yourself to, play to their personality and present what's important to them. (Segel, 2018)

Ask questions...then listen – There will be gaps in your knowledge about a prospect or opportunity. Unless you understand the problem completely, you may not be able to solve their issue. For this reason, it's critical to ask intuitive and thoughtful questions during your conversations. Lots of them.

Here are some examples:

- "What are you looking for?"
- "What are the critical items?"
- "Has it always been this way?"
- "How should this product be processed?"
- "What are you doing to address the problem?"

Have a list of questions prepared. This will indicate your interest and guide the conversation. Once you've asked a question, actively listen. Focus on what the manager is saying and pay attention to their mannerisms and gestures. Don't just wait to speak. Then, after they've finished their thought, communicate their message back to them: "So, you're saying that your production is down?" or "Your ideal candidate has strong communication skills." Actively listen—and respond with some insight. This helps you to get a grip on the problem, and helps them feel comfortable.

Remember you're selling to a person – When you're consistently asking for job opportunities, it's easy to forget you are selling to a person...and they want to be treated as such. Treat others the same way you would like to be treated. Would you like getting the email you're about to send? The voicemail? If not, there's a good chance the hiring manager won't, either.

Be professional and personable. Everyone has lives and families outside of work. Let your conversation drift to personal. It can't be all business all the time.

> If you want to land an awesome job upon graduating—and I mean awesome, not, "Hey I got lucky and ABC Engineering up the road offered me a gig."—I mean interesting, fulfilling work on a great team... you need to develop a network in your chosen field in advance of walking across the stage. If you have target companies, you will improve your chances of landing an interview and a job offer by taking the time to develop a network (cultivating genuine relationships) to help you get there. Having a more senior level person interested in helping you in your career and willing to advocate on your behalf is of immeasurable benefit.
>
> **Mel Butcher** – Host of the Empowering Women Podcast, Industrial Water Engineer

Chapter 6—What You Learned

It's time to get yourself out there. To land the position you want, you need to get out of your comfort zone and start networking. Remember, the connections you make along the way may last a lifetime.

Action Items:

- Work on your conversation skills. Practice with people you encounter during a normal day.
- Start networking. Reach out to your connections, family, friends, fellow students, and professors. Ask them questions about where you can find engineering professionals.

7

Reach out to Gain Opportunities

"Opportunities don't often come along. So, when they do, you have to grab them."
—Audrey Hepburn

Where to Look

Trying to land a job can be frustrating. It takes more time, energy, and patience than it should. The only thing you can do is to send out more résumés, right? Wrong.

Do some homework. Doing your homework on companies beforehand can have huge benefits on your networking and make you more likely to land a job. Target specific companies and reach out to them, rather than relying on a résumé and online applications.

The more applications you complete, the more likely you are to get a positive response...but are they opportune responses? Are you willing to accept whatever job comes along? Alternatively, are you looking to set yourself apart for an excellent career? Rather than applying online hundreds of times, consider spending your time with a few top-notch companies and learn as much as you can. Here are sources that can help:

Glassdoor – It's a vast resource where employees can leave anonymous information about their salary, benefits, opinions of their employers, and plenty more.

LinkedIn – This professional online gathering place can help you network and land a job. Search for the name of the company you want to apply to and see what information you can gather about the people who work there.

Social media – Most career advisors aren't going to tell you to look to Twitter to get a job, but you never know what's going to help you get you a foot in the door. Twitter can be a great way to break the ice with people that work at a company that interests you.

Company web site – You may be able to find a company directory of the people you'll work with.

Once you get a picture of what particular company is like, you can get a better idea of whether you'd want to work there and if their values, pay, benefits and environment match what you are looking for.

Okay...so now you have an idea of the industry you would like to work in, and you've pinpointed some exciting companies. You have an extraordinary résumé and are ready to impress. If you haven't initiated conversations, you need to start. Start tracking down key people, like hiring managers, HR managers, and technical recruiters.

Treat hiring managers like human beings:

- Don't be afraid to reach out.
- If you're cold-emailing, be professional.
- Don't ask for a favor the first time you talk.
- Don't get upset if they don't respond quickly.
- Don't pester them if they don't respond.
- If you think it may be creepy or rude, it is.

Lastly, do not forget your alumni association. They have essential information that could help you land a position. They have been there for you before, and may be able to help you now.

Engineering Organizations

Looking for a place to start networking? Use the information below to start your search and pick what interests you. Connect with a club, society, or conference and join in. Remember, engineering societies and clubs want you! Young engineers are their future.

Start by searching the web for the following:

- *Engineer(ing) society [city near you]*
- *Engineer(ing) club [city near you]*
- *Engineer(ing) conference [city near you]*

Consider reaching out to the following societies that fit into your particular field. You are the future of their society, and they desperately want you to join. Engineering clubs, societies, and organizations often offer membership for very little money, and they come with great opportunities for networking.

- American Academy of Environmental Engineers
- American Association of Engineering Societies
- American Helicopter Society
- American Institute of Aeronautics and Astronautics
- American Institute of Chemical Engineers
- American Nuclear Society
- American Railway Engineering Association
- American Society for Engineering Education
- American Society of Agricultural and Biological Engineers
- American Society of Civil Engineers
- American Society of Heating, Refrigerating and Air-Conditioning Engineers
- American Society of Mechanical Engineers
- American Society of Naval Engineers
- American Society of Plumbing Engineers
- American Society of Safety Engineers
- American Society for Nondestructive Testing
- American Welding Society
- Architectural Engineering Institute
- ASM International
- Association for Computing Machinery
- Audio Engineering Society
- Biomedical Engineering Society
- Institute of Biological Engineering
- Institute of Electrical and Electronics Engineers
- Institute of Industrial and Systems Engineers
- Institute of Transportation Engineers
- National Society of Black Engineers
- National Society of Professional Engineers

- Order of the Engineer
- Society for the Advancement of Material and Process Engineering
- Society of American Military Engineers
- Society of Automotive Engineers
- Society of Broadcast Engineers
- Society of Fire Protection Engineers
- Society of Hispanic Professional Engineers
- Society of Manufacturing Engineers
- Society of Naval Architects and Marine Engineers
- Society of Petroleum Engineers
- Society of Women Engineers

Online Branding

LinkedIn is a powerful tool for students and graduates to start a network. It can help define your career path, build a professional network, and even find a job.

> *"Your brand is what other people say about you when you're not in the room."*
> *—Jeff Bezos*

For job hunting, gathering leads, or networking, having a professional, eye-catching LinkedIn profile is an excellent way to get found by the right people at the right time. The more complete your LinkedIn profile, the better the odds that recruiters and hiring managers will find you. Be sure you complete your entire profile. Recruiters and hiring managers want to know what skills you have, what your experiences are, where you're located, and what people are saying about you. LinkedIn measures the "completeness" of your profile. Be sure you are "All-Star." Here are some important best practices you should follow to make your profile as powerful as possible:

- Update your status; frequently comment and like posts; share regularly.
- Make 500+ connections in your industry.
- Continuously maintain and add new connections.
- Give and then ask for recommendations, skills, and endorsements.

Banner photo – A banner photo should be inviting, bright, and high quality. Use something appealing. I also suggest using something related to your industry or your hobbies. Find a high-quality photo online that you can use on your profile.

Try Unsplash or Pixaby apps for free high-quality images.

Professional photo – Start with a professional headshot. If you don't have a professional photo, get one. Until you get your professional photo, use the cleanest, most professional looking snapshot you have. Not a selfie! Be sure to smile! Your profile picture may be your first impression with a potential employer. Seriously, smile!

Not sure what "professional" means? Look around at what other engineers are using and imitate the best you can find. How do you know if you've got a great photo? Test it on Photofeeler (**www.photofeeler.com**). People will vote on how your photo looks across three different professional categories: competence, likable, and influential. These are the most important aspects of the photo. You'll be surprised which photo people like the best.

Contact information and URL for your profile – Be sure to include contact information. It's important for hiring managers to reach you quickly. It's much easier to broadcast your profile with a customized URL (ideally linkedin.com/your name), rather than the heavy combination of numbers that LinkedIn automatically assigns you. How do you get one?

On the Edit Profile screen, at the bottom of the gray window that shows your basic information, you'll see a Public Profile URL. Click "Edit" next to the URL, and specify what you'd like your address to be. When you're finished, click Set Custom URL. This is also nice for adding the URL to your résumé or putting it on a business card. It looks nice and is easy to remember.

Headline – Make your headline stand out. By default, LinkedIn uses your headline with your job title and current company. Don't leave it that way. List your specialty as if you are speaking directly to a potential hiring manager. Remember to include relevant keywords. This increases your odds of being found in searches both on LinkedIn and Google. Try to keep your headline to about ten words.

Your headline doesn't need to be your job title and company... and if you're looking for a job, it shouldn't be. Instead, use that space to display your specialty and you're "so what?" The more specifics you provide about what sets you apart, the better. Here are some examples.

- Mechanical Engineer – Seeking Entry Level Position
- Electrical Engineering Graduate – Seeking Opportunity
- Civil Engineering Student – Seeking Internship

Let's walk through your LinkedIn Profile step-by-step. Here's the graphic from the page where users will learn about you:

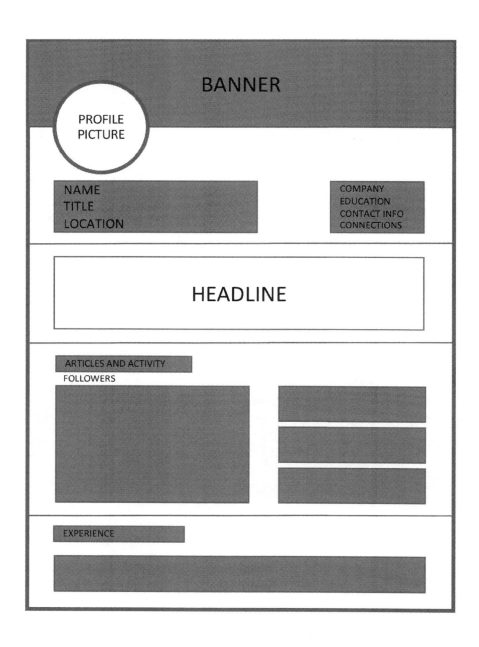

EDUCATION

VOLUNTEER EXPERIENCE

SKILLS AND ENDORSEMENTS

RECOMMENDATIONS

ACCOMPLISHMENTS

INTERESTS

Summary – According to LinkedIn, the summary is the #1 most-read section. As a job hunter, you cannot afford to go easy on this section.

Look at the descriptions of the positions you're after and use a word cloud on websites like Wordle (www.wordle.net). Copy and paste your summary text into the site and see what pops up. Is your summary saying what you want it to say? Does it match job descriptions in which you are interested?

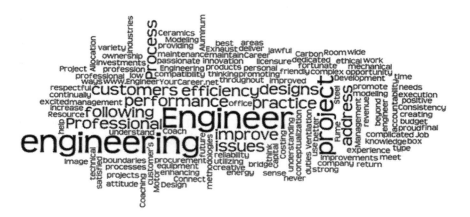

See those words that stand out? Those standout words populate your profile in the search bar for LinkedIn and Google. Consider revising until your word cloud represents your ideal position.

Fill out the summary field with a few of your most significant achievements. Use bullets to make this easy to read. Think about your target employer and what you can offer to make their lives easier.

"Much like the rest of your résumé, you'll want to highlight past results in your summary. When possible, include numbers and case studies that prove success. Social media consultant and speaker Wayne Breitbarth, for example, quickly establishes credibility with his audience by stating in his summary's second sentence: 'I have helped more than 40,000 businesspeople—from entry-level to CEO—understand how to use LinkedIn effectively.' Never underestimate the power of a few key stats to impress a reader."
(Muse, 2019)

Media – Did you know that you can add media files to your experience section? It's a great way to present a visual portfolio along with your résumé.

Experience – Keep your work history up to date. There's no need to list every job, only the jobs relevant to your current career goals. Be sure to list your internships.

Link your job to the company. When you link your experience on LinkedIn, you are prompted for the name of a company that you worked for. If they have a profile, link your experience to that company and show the company's logo on your profile. When others look at the company's profile, you will be listed as an employee.

Give the reader an overview of the tasks and accomplishments you completed. Include some keywords, facts, and figures. So, for example, if you were an intern, what did you do and what did you accomplish? Use action words such as managed, led, grew, reduced, saved, etc. Don't overdo the bullets. Try to stick to three or four.

Education – This section is pretty self-explanatory. Make sure to list all of your education. Even high school, if you'd like.

Volunteer Experience – Be sure to put something here. List anything that is relevant or brands you as a leader, like University Engineering Club, Student Government, Toastmasters™, etc.

Skills and Endorsements – Get 20 endorsements for the three top skills. Skills should be based on the attributes of your career. Stay away from skills like Microsoft Word. This is a given and generally means nothing. Skills like engineering, project management, sales, and 3D modeling, however, can help your profile.

Recommendations – Ask for recommendations. Endorsements are great, but recommendations are currency on LinkedIn. Reach out to friends, colleagues, managers, and associates and ask that they write you a recommendation. Three to five solid recommendations can mean a lot to a prospective employer or recruiter. To get recommendations, you need to give recommendations. Reach out to some students, professors, or friends to start.

Accomplishments – Lots of items could go under this category. Spend some time to fill this out. I do not recommend listing every class you had in college, given that your degrees are listed. But what about special projects? Courses outside of your degree? Extracurricular activities?

Interests – Connect with other networks and websites. Join 12 groups related to your industry. These are great spots to find engineers like yourself. The bigger the group, the better.

Bad Publicity

Personal branding is essential. Showing and demonstrating who you are via your social media platforms opens up doors. Social media and networking have become the preferred method of communication, and your information can be found online by your potential new employer. By modifying your available information, you can turn social media into a positive or a negative when looking for a new job.

Here are social media mistakes that could ruin an opportunity:

- Risqué or racy content
- Offensive sentiments or images
- Extreme political or religious views
- Photos or discussion of illegal activities (even if you're joking)
- Images and updates that reference partying and getting crazy
- Angry or argumentative comments and threads

You can be yourself on social media, as long as you are aware of your presence and use restraint. Don't talk about partying, new tattoos, or how much you hate something. I'd even refrain from extreme political views. No photos of you drunk. Not even with an alcoholic drink in your hand. Even if it's amusing. You can, however, send it to me, but it must be hilarious.

Make sure your profile photos on every social media site you use are professional and friendly. Not sure if they are or not? Use Photofeeler.

Think of it this way. Don't place anything on social media that you wouldn't want your boss to see. This is especially true on LinkedIn.

Cold Emailing

Cold emailing* is a strategy that involves reaching out via email to someone who may not know you. It's similar to cold calling; you're getting in touch with someone without meeting, being introduced, or hearing from them first. Why do you cold email?

To find a job. Cold emailing is a strategy to get your foot in the door with your target companies. Are you not having luck networking? Are you trying to find a job in another state? Find dozens of companies you want to work for and start cold emailing.

Tips when cold emailing someone:

- Provide a compelling, clear subject line.
- Personalize the introduction with their name.
- Don't get right to the question; show the recipient you have some context about them. Flattery works well.
- Tell them why you're reaching out, clearly and concisely.
- Say "thank you."
- Keep the message short and direct.
- Don't get upset if they don't respond.
- If they tell you to contact them at another time, put it in your calendar and reach out respectfully.
- Be persistent but polite.
    *See Cold Email template – Chapter 11

Finding and Working with Recruiters

A technical recruiter is a valuable asset, even if you're not looking for a new position right now. Technical recruiters are focused on specialized industries—like IT or engineering—and are hired to match the brightest talents in technology fields with the companies that need their expertise.

The employer pays a technical recruiter once they hire a candidate. Recruiters don't work for job seekers. Recruiters are generally delighted to work with young professionals, whether those professionals have qualifications that meet their current assignment or not.

Search LinkedIn for technical recruiters who typically place professionals with your skill set. Most will advertise themselves as "Technical Recruiter." Some will be specific, focusing on engineering, programming, or another technical field. Most will gladly accept an invitation to connect.

Make it easy for recruiters to find you by making yourself visible:

- Create a professional presence on LinkedIn.
- Be active in trade and professional associations.
- Be active in your community.
- Consider writing articles, or starting a website or blog.

Once you have connected with a recruiter, tailor your communications to each recruiter's preferences. An exceptional résumé will always put you in good standing with recruiters, but check with the recruiting firms you contact for their résumé preferences. Ask how they prefer to be contacted (phone? email?) and stay in touch periodically...but don't be a pest. An initial follow-up call after you submit your materials, and then again two weeks later is a good rule of thumb. If you update your résumé, resubmit it, or contact the recruiter to relay the new information.

Ask key questions as you decide whether or not you want to work with them. Ask about their experience with your industry. Inquire about the recruiter's process. Then conduct research, including among members of your network, to get a feel for the recruiter's reputation, and decide whether to proceed with this recruiter. You need someone that will understand your needs and desires.

Below are general tips to use when working with a recruiter:

- Once you are in the process of applying for a job with a recruiter, don't contact the employer directly. Doing so is going over the recruiter's head.

- Don't back out of your commitment once you have agreed to be a candidate. Be willing to see the process through.

- Trust the recruiter. They have the experience and wisdom to give you the best advice as you work through the process.

- Discuss your offer. Recruiters have great advice and can help you determine if the offer is fair.

- Thank your recruiter at the end of the process. A simple thank-you goes a long way toward cementing your relationship.

- Be open to contact from the recruiter even after you've landed a job. You never know when you might need the recruiter again.

- Serve as a resource to recruiters after you have the job. You may need their help in the future. If you help them, they will return the favor.

- Never work with a recruiter that asks you to pay for their services.

Fake Job Posts

Fake job posts are everywhere. They often anger and disappoint job seekers. Why would someone create a fake job post and waste the time of all the applicants? A phony job post, although frustrating, can generate lots of information for others.

Employers can use fake job posts to gauge the talent pool. It is a way for them to see what talent is available. This information can be used to hire or even replace current employees.

Employers and recruiters can use your résumé to stockpile information for a later date. Recruiters are paid when a candidate is hired based on the client's needs. A database full of résumés is significant to a recruiter's success. The more résumés, the more likely they can find a candidate.

Fake job postings also exist so that people can spam you. Make sure you are applying to jobs directly on company websites.

If it appears that your résumé disappeared into a black hole, it doesn't necessarily mean the job was fake. Often, we never know why we don't hear back from employers. It could be the volume of applicants, or the position was never filled.

Not receiving feedback from an application is disappointing, but it's going to happen. Before you invest your time applying, do your best to determine if the job posting is genuine. Does it appear on the company's website? Is the job title uncoordinated with the pay range? A little research today can save you a lot of time and frustration.

> The purpose of networking is to build relationships and knowledge. You need to get the name and contact info of who you're talking to. Sounds simple, but time after time we waste the opportunity to follow up or build a relationship further by either being afraid to ask for contact info or forgetting. There's no excuse. I'm a bit old fashioned, but I'm a huge fan of business cards for networking. Yes, many people don't bother with cards anymore, but I have many contacts that I would never have been able to build a relationship with, if we had not exchanged cards.
>
> **Crystal G. Morrison**, Ph.D. – Founder & CEO at EverRise

Chapter 7—What You Learned

You are well on your way. You've learned what it takes to land a job offer, brand yourself, set up a great LinkedIn profile, network, work with recruiters, avoid fake job posts, and collect the contacts it takes to land some interviews. You should be excited! Let's get you ready for some interviews.

Action Items:

- Get networking. Hustle.

- Connect with as many engineers as you can. Use LinkedIn, cold emailing, your friends, family, networking events, engineering clubs, job fairs, and conferences—anything you can find.

- Do your research if you are applying to online postings; apply and then move on. Don't waste your energy thinking about it. Use your energy for connecting to others.

8

Ace Interviews

*"During job interviews, when they ask:
'What is your worst quality?' I always say:
'Flatulence.' That way I get my own office."*
–Dan Thompson

Preparations

To impress a hiring manager, you must be able to describe your strengths and career goals confidently in thirty seconds or less. The more compelling the story, the better chance for success. Sell your ability to contribute. Reflect on your past, assess yourself, and portray a summary of what kind of engineer you are and what you can accomplish in the future. Be honest, be authentic, and be yourself. Remember, it's not what you have done but what you can do for the company.

Prepare, prepare, and prepare some more.

Most engineers know they need to show up to the interview having done their homework, but most do not prepare enough. You should find out as much as possible about the company, the organization, its culture, their industries, and the interviewer. It never hurts to ask others about specific job challenges. Then you can demonstrate that you have what it takes to fill the job requirements.

Formulate a strategy.

During your preparations, decide what three or four messages you want to convey to the interviewer. They should align with the job description. Use stories. Your stories should be concise and compelling. Make sure the stories have a good opening line, such as, "I'm going to tell you about a time that I worked with a team for a class project." Then, practice. Practice enough to confidently answer many interview questions with a few great stories.

- Write stories of your successes. Make the stories broad enough to apply to a range of interview questions.
- Practice your stories, record them, and watch them. Repeat until you feel comfortable. Aim for thirty seconds each.
- Print out the job posting and write how you will fulfill each requirement using your accomplishments.

Help the interviewer and yourself by answering questions with detail and following up with the right questions.

For example, if the interviewer asks if you have experience with AutoCAD, you can say, "Yes, I have AutoCAD experience." Or, you can clarify the answer and ask another: "Yes, I have AutoCAD and AutoCAD 3D Inventor experience. How often do you expect me to use AutoCAD?"

Emphasize your potential.

Job candidates aren't perfect—and that includes you. Instead of discussing where you lack experience, focus on your potential. If your achievements are not directly related to the job, but you can demonstrate the ability to learn and adapt, you must clearly articulate this. For example, if you're interviewing for a designer role but have no design experience, explain how your abilities in machine design or fluids address your ability to design a particular product.

It is important that you emphasize your plan to master all aspects of the job, and mention growth in the role and within the company. Emphasize your intent of a long career at the company.

Don't just be yourself...

...be the best version of you. Bring as much energy and enthusiasm to the interview as you can without overselling yourself. Employers are wary that people may be exaggerating their experience and skills. Make sure you can back up any statement about achievements with evidence.

Interview Flow

If you don't have interview experience, or it's been a while since you've been in the job market, knowing what items may be covered can be useful preparation. Plan to do the following things in the interview:

- Introduce yourself.
- Discuss your background.
- State why you're applying to the job.
- Review the job description and requirements.

- Answer the interview questions.
- State what you can do for the firm.
- Affirm why they should hire you.
- Ask questions.
- Wrap up the interview.
- Follow up with an email.

First Impressions

When interview prepping, focus on the difficult questions, the responses you'll give, and the witty-yet-professional anecdotes you'll tell to land you an offer letter. From the moment you walk in the door for that interview, however, you must make a stellar first impression...because before you even get the chance to deliver those impeccable answers, you'll have eyes judging you, evaluating your fit to the team and the company.

Make sure you're presenting yourself properly and setting yourself up for a successful interview.

Be early.

If you're early, you're on time. If you're on time, you're late. Being punctual is a given.

Are you running late? Call as soon as possible to let your interviewers know. They will appreciate information ahead of time versus an excuse later.

As my grandmother says, "Dress like the bee's knees."

Your appearance won't be the basis of the job offer, but it can certainly ruin it. When you show up in your Sunday best with your polished résumé, you'll come across as a top-notch professional.

On the other hand, if you're dressed as if you are home lying around on the couch, juggling your briefcase, purse, and a stack of wrinkled résumés, you're probably not going to appear as a professional.

Bring only the essentials.

Coffee may be necessary for you to wake up, but don't bring your paper cup inside the office to finish it off. The same goes for other non-essentials, like the granola bar you're polishing off. These things may not eliminate your chances, but they're not going to put you in the most favorable light.

Be nice to everyone.

The receptionist may not be the hiring manager, but that doesn't mean their opinion of you won't matter. If you have a lousy demeanor at the front door, it will get back to the hiring manager. It's important to treat everyone just as well as you'll address the interviewer.

No phones.

It's natural to want to use your phone when you have to wait, but if you're waiting in the lobby, don't. Instead, take that time to review your résumé, interviewer questions, and names of your interviewers. When your interviewer makes their appearance, you don't want to be caught off guard, closing Snapchat and stuffing your phone back into your pocket.

Make your documents organized and accessible.

Almost as soon as the interview starts, you'll need a copy of your résumé. Make sure you don't have to dig through your candy wrappers, chargers, and other documents to find it; you don't want to appear disorganized. Everything you need must be readily accessible. You should be able to pull out your résumé, references, and even a pen, on command.

Start the interview.

How you enter the room, speak, and how comfortable you look are important. Be sure to speak clearly and slowly.

You can expect the interviewer to make the first introductions, but don't be afraid to start the handshakes. It's a small gesture, but it says that you are excited to be there, confident, and self-assured. Be sure to make eye contact and smile as you shake hands.

Make a connection.

After the introductions, nail your first impression by making a connection with the interviewer. Find something you have in common and chat about it. Making a connection can help your interviewer realize "This might work." Draw out details that will get you that "in": "Oh, you're from Pittsburgh? I love Pittsburgh—How about the Pirates this year?"

These tips themselves may not win you the job, but they will certainly get you closer to landing that next opportunity.

S.O.A.R Method

When you are networking, interviewing, or even storytelling, consider the S.O.A.R. method. The S.O.A.R. method keeps you focused on the discussion and provides a complete story. It helps you portray the point.

S – Situation

Explain the context in the form of a real-life story. This is the "before" picture which shows what was happening at the time of the situation: "I was in a meeting with more than thirty people in Italy trying to portray an idea."

O – Obstacle

Define the issue or issues that caused the problem. This will inform the interviewer what you had to overcome: "I only spoke English, and they were speaking Italian."

A – Action

Explain the action you took to resolve the situation: "I found a translator and analyzed the ideas, speaking clearly and slowly before waiting for the translator to finish."

R – Results

Share the outcome and the important knowledge you gained: "The project became more efficient, and now I can understand more Italian."

Interview Q&As

The following questions are typical for an interview. Use these questions and responses as practice. Don't practice by reading; give these to someone else to practice multiple mock interviews with you. You will be more effective giving answers in real-time and getting feedback. Consider recording yourself answering these questions and then playing them back for improvement. Practice, practice, and practice some more to win your next opportunity.

Tell me about yourself.

Give the employer an overview of who you are and do it professionally. You should prepare an approximately one-minute-long answer that summarizes your career, your strengths, and your most recent job. Keep personal life out of it.

What are your weaknesses?

Address this by minimizing your weaknesses and emphasizing your strengths. No personal qualities, only professional traits: "I am working on improving my public speaking, and I recently joined Toastmasters™." State the issue, and then say how you are turning it into a strength.

Why should I hire you?

Summarize your experiences and demonstrate how they can help the employer. The more you know about the company, the easier it is to connect the two. "I have a record of successful projects that would make a big difference in your company. I'm confident I would be a great addition to your project team."

What do you know about our company?

Interviewers want to see if you have a sense of how the company works. What makes the company different from its competition? How does it make money? What are the company's specialties? If it seems as though you have not done this basic research, your interviewer will wonder how interested you are.

Why do you want to work here?

The interviewer is listening for an answer that indicates you have given this some thought and are not sending out blanket résumés. This is your chance to prove why they should hire you. State your skills, be confident, and tell the employer why they want you. Match your skills to the job description.

Why would you excel at this job?

This is your chance to make a case for why you would shine in the job. If you do not know the answer, it is unlikely your interviewer will hire you. You should have a firm response that states your skills and record of accomplishment. Both should relate to the needs of the employer.

What interests you about the job?

How does the role interest you? Only talk about the day-to-day work you would be doing, not the benefits, salary, or short commute. Interviewers want to hire people who like their work. You need to convince the employer that you will enjoy the job.

What are your goals?

It is best to talk about short-term and intermediate goals rather than locking yourself into the distant future. For example, "My immediate goal is to get a rewarding job in a growth-oriented company. My long-term goal will depend on where the company goes. I hope to grow into a position of responsibility."

What would you do in your first 90 days in this position?

Reveal how you set goals and solve problems. The employer wants to know whether you are ambitious without being unrealistic. You should also acknowledge that you would need to take time to understand procedures, the team, customers, or vendors.

Tell me about a time when...

Good interviewers will ask about times you had to exercise the skills required for the job. These may be situations when you had to take the initiative, deal with a difficult customer, or solve a problem for a client. Prepare for these questions with S.O.A.R. stories, so you are not struggling to think of real examples. Brainstorm two stories that you can use to answer these questions. The story should discuss the problem you faced, the response, and the outcome you achieved.

What is most important to you in a new position?

Interviewers want to understand your career goals and whether this job will fulfill you. After all, if you are looking for a job with customer contact and this job is mostly solo work, it might not be the right fit for you. It is in your best interest to be candid and specific when you answer this, so you land in a job that aligns with your goals.

What can you do for us that other candidates cannot?

This is an assessment of your experiences, skills, and traits. Summarize: "I have a combination of strong technical skills, and the ability to work well with others. This allows me to share my knowledge with others on your team."

Describe a difficult work situation and what you did to overcome it.

This is similar to question 11. The interviewer wants to hear how you overcame the situation and how you solved it. This is a problem-solving question that tests your critical thinking skills. Have two S.O.A.R stories ready to convince the employer that you have worked through a difficult situation successfully. This could be at school or in the context of a part-time job. Try to avoid co-worker related problems unless you had to fire someone.

What are three positive things your last boss or professor would say about you?

It is time to pull out your old performance reviews and brag about yourself through someone else's words: "My boss has told me that I am the best designer he has ever had. He knows he can rely on me, and he likes my sense of humor."

What is your greatest accomplishment?

This may be part of an answer to "Tell me about yourself." If you do not include this part in your response to that question, the interviewer may ask about your greatest achievements. Do you have your Fundamentals of Engineering certificate? Any unique difficulties you overcame? Were you on the deans' list?

Where do you see yourself in five years?

For employers, it is vital to hire employees who have the potential for further personal growth. They are looking for candidates that understand their career goals and objectives, and whether or not they are highly motivated toward the position. Do they seriously consider their job search and career objectives? Do they just want to get a foot in the door, or are they going to bring value to the company? They want their employees to be interested in the future of the company and remain loyal to it.

What salary are you seeking?

There are two ways to answer. The first is to be honest and state your desired salary, or give a range. If you have done some research, you should know what the typical salary is for your field and area. Either tactic can work to your advantage, but it is best to start your relationship with honesty. Once you have your offer, you know they want you. That is when you can negotiate. The second way can be used if you are entirely unsure of the salary; simply ask, "What do you typically pay for a person in my situation?"

What questions do you have for me?

At the end of every job interview, you will likely be asked if you have any questions. At this stage, ask open-ended questions about office culture and role clarification.

Behavioral Questions

Employers use behavioral interview questions to determine if your skills and abilities align with the position. These types of questions can also reveal if your personality will fit the company culture. They want to determine how you will handle certain situations within the role.

Make sure you prepare for the questions before an interview. It's challenging to predict the interview questions, but the job description should give you an idea. Make use of the S.O.A.R. method to answer these questions with stories from your experiences. Consider how you would answer questions in the following areas:

Teamwork – Teamwork is crucial for engineers. Chances are you will receive at least one question about your experience collaborating with co-workers. For example:

- Tell me about a time when you had to work closely with others. Did you have any difficulties with personalities?
- How did you handle any conflict on the team?
- Do you find working in a team rewarding?
- What is the most challenging part of working in a team?

Communication – Candidates often overlook communication questions. You communicate every day with numerous people and may consider yourself adequate. However, you need to have examples ready to answer these questions. Employers are always aware of how poor communication can lose time and money. They want to make sure you are part of the solution, not the problem:

- Tell me about a successful presentation you've given.
- Give an example of when you've effectively used written communication to explain complex problems.
- Have you developed relationships with co-workers in your current role?
- Have you ever given a presentation on the spot?

Time management – Unless you work for the government, you must be efficient. Prioritizing is essential for you to be productive. Employers will want you to juggle multiple assignments and need to know that you will still make deadlines:

- Tell me about a time you had multiple responsibilities. How did you handle it?
- What do you do when work gets overwhelming?
- How do you handle interruptions or distractions?
- How do you keep projects on schedule?

Client-facing skills – No matter what type of engineer you are, you will interact with customers. Employers want to be comfortable that you will keep the customer happy. They want you to go beyond regular duties to gain repeat business:

- What do you do with a difficult customer/client?
- Tell me about a time when you gave a client excellent customer service.
- Tell me about a time you failed to meet a customer's expectations.

Initiative – Hiring managers want to know you're dedicated. It's your job to convince them that you will go above and beyond. They want you to be self-motivated, and know that you are not going to give up easily. They want a problem solver, not a creator:

- Describe a project or idea that was put into place because of your efforts. What was your role and what was the result?
- Talk about a time that your initiative caused change.
- Give an example of a setback. How did you handle it?
- Describe a time when you failed. How did you overcome it?
- Give an example of a time when you saw a problem and used it as an opportunity instead. What was the result? What would you have done differently?

- Describe a time where you initiated a project or change. What did you do, and how did it turn out?

Leadership – You'll come across questions to assess your leadership skills. Maybe the position has potential for advancement, or the employer wants to see if you have the potential. Regardless, you'll get leadership questions, even if you haven't experienced a leadership role:

- Describe a time when you were in a leadership role.
- Tell us about a time you took the lead on a project.
- Tell us about a time you led by example.
- Talk about a leadership role you've had outside of work.
- What was the hardest group or team that you've had to lead? Why?
- How did you handle difficult co-workers or situations?

Don't go into your next interview without preparing for the behavioral questions. One of these questions could be your next great opportunity.

Answer the Unexpected

Out of nowhere, you may get questions like "If you were an animal, which one would you be?" or "What's your most awkward moment?" Don't fret. These questions are intentionally silly to get you out of your comfort zone, to see how you handle the unexpected. Don't be a deer in headlights. Follow these tips:

- Smile. It helps. Your reaction, ideally, should show how confident and unfazed you are. Smiling and laughing shows you're unfazed.
- Buy yourself some time to think by commenting on the question. For example: "That's a great question! Let me think about that," "I've never been asked that before," or "I thought I had prepared for anything. Let's see…"

- Answer the question enthusiastically. These types of questions don't have a correct answer. The key to responding is using enthusiasm and coherence. If you can manage a joke, great.

- Don't get too wrapped up trying to convince the interviewer you're insightful. Respond coherently, smile, and move on.

- Lastly, start a conversation about it! A great way to complete your response is to ask your interviewer how others responded. Want to turn the tables? Ask them their answer. It's a nice way to demonstrate your interest in the interviewer.

Questions for the Interviewer

Interviewers will conclude by asking, "Do you have any questions?" The interviewer will use these questions to gauge your interest in and understanding of the job. Don't miss this opportunity. If you do not ask questions, you'll appear uninterested.

You need to determine if the opportunity is a good fit for you. Be sure to ask questions that will enable you to understand the job adequately, so that you can make an informed decision about working for the company. Be sure to ask about the next steps in the hiring process and the employer's timeline for getting back to you.

The following list contains topics for you to discuss in the initial job interview and ones to avoid. You should also develop questions during your research of the company.

Practicing these interviewer questions will ensure you are prepared when you get the chance.

What does a typical day look like for this role?

This question can help you decide if this is a job you want, and shows your interest in the position itself. Job goals and company mission statements are nice to know, but the day-to-day of the job is critical to your enjoyment.

What are the greatest challenges for this role, and your company/department?

This question shows that you're thinking about the job itself, and the answers will help you evaluate the role. Maybe the day-to-day tasks are not what you pictured or are interested in. Alternatively, the company challenges may help you realize you wouldn't function well in their atmosphere.

What's the company culture like?

This question helps to determine how comfortable you might be working there. If you can ask this question to multiple interviewers, you may see some patterns in their answers. The patterns will help you determine what it's like to work there.

What can you tell me about the team I would be working with?

You can use this question to gather more company information and specific responsibilities of the team.

Why does your company have job openings?

The answer to this question helps you evaluate whether you may have problems with the company in the future. For instance, did the company lose engineers because of a bad environment? Layoffs? Low wages? Retirement? Restructuring?

What does a long-term career look like at this company?

This question says you're thinking long-term...which companies want—*desperately* want. Hiring and training are expensive. It also gives you an idea of the opportunities that may be in your future. You can learn more about the specific role you're applying for—and about future roles. This question will help you learn about your potential career options. How quickly will you hit a glass ceiling? How soon will you get a promotion?

How has the company changed in the past few years?

This question could uncover a pile of great information you could use. You'll get a better sense of where the company is headed and learn about its past. You may also uncover the amount and types of changes in the company culture and leadership.

What is your favorite / least favorite thing about working for this company?

This question can assist in determining pros and cons as you consider whether this company is right for you. You need to ask this question to multiple interviewers to get real answers. Often, the hiring manager will feed you bland answers like, "I enjoy the work that we do," or "We have communication issues."

What are your expectations for the first 90 days?

It takes some time to get up to speed in a new job. There's training, standards, procedures, new tools, and all kinds of different people. These are all items you need to understand before being productive. It is helpful to know what the hiring manager or team expects from you. This will help you focus on specific goals and questions in your interviews.

Each job interview question is an opportunity to highlight your skills and learn more about the opportunities you're pursuing.

Topics to avoid in an early interview:

- Salary
- Benefits
- Vacation, sick days, personal days, or time off
- Details that you should already know based on the job description or company website
- Publicly available information

Phone Interview

Why do some employers prefer phone interviews? To avoid wasting time and resources on candidates who turn out not to be a good fit. A phone interview is often your first point of contact with the company. You're not going to land the job from the phone interview, but you can certainly lose it.

At their core, phone interviews are very similar to in-person interviews. Treat them just as seriously. You're going to have to work just as hard to make sure you are coming off as a personable, capable, and adequate candidate.

Focus and cut out all distractions.

Turn off the TV. Mute doesn't work; it may still distract you. No one is interested in hearing how the Paw Patrol is saving the day.

Get comfortable, but not too comfortable. Don't slouch.

Sit at the kitchen table or a desk and have all your materials ready for easy access. One benefit of interviewing by phone is that you can place all of the materials and notes in front of you. Prepare a cheat sheet.

Be ready for common phone interview questions:

- Are you willing to relocate for this job?
- Will you travel for this job?
- What interests you about this job?
- If you are hired, when can you start?

Follow Up

Always send a thank-you email* after an interview. Few candidates do this, but it is yet another way to stand out and make a good impression. Use specific topics from the interview and restate your interest in the company and the position. Better yet, handwrite the letter on a generic card, making sure it is neat and legible. According to Reuters.com:

- Only 24% of job applicants bother to send thank-you notes.
- 80% of human resource managers surveyed felt that thank you notes were useful in evaluating potential hires.

(Taylor, 2019)

If you met with several people, send each of them an individual thank-you letter or email. Remember to keep it short. Proofread it carefully and send promptly.

Best practices for thank-you notes or emails:

- Ask for a business card at each interview so that you will have the necessary contact information.
- Send within one or two days of the interview.
- Send a personalized email or letter to every person who interviewed you.
- Keep the length to five or six sentences.
- Express your continued interest in the position.
- Personalize the note by referring to something the interviewer mentioned.
- Remind the person of a few of your strengths that make you a good match.
- Proofread.

If you don't hear back within a week, send an email to ask where they are in the hiring process. Be patient. Hiring can take a long time.

*See thank-you letter template for more information.

Finish Strong

If you are being invited to interviews but still not landing the job, start by dissecting the steps related to that turning point:

- Are you fully preparing?
- Are you showing that you're passionate, interesting, and engaged?
- Are you asking about next steps before you leave the interview?

- Are you sending a thoughtful, timely, and professional thank-you email? Your competition is doing all of these things. Are you?

Take the time to tweak the fundamentals and not miss a single step. Perfecting your strategy will often result in positive momentum, allow you to refocus, and eliminate weeks of frustration.

What Not to Do in an Interview

Do not disappear into the chair and answer questions with a one-word answer. You are a professional. Whenever possible, turn your answer into a question: "Yes, I have AutoCAD experience. How much time will I spend making or checking drawings?"

Never ask the interviewer, "Do you think I'm qualified for the job?" or "What are my chances?" What does it matter what the interviewer thinks right now? They have not had a chance to consider if you meet the qualifications. Be confident. Don't ask the interviewer, "Do you like me?" or, "Am I doing okay?"

Don't beg: "I really, really want this job!" or "I need this job!"

When you don't have experience in something particular that the interviewer asks you about, say "I haven't used that tool yet—but I'm a quick learner!" If you grovel, you will drive away the right managers and bring in the wrong ones.

Don't spend all your energy trying to please the interviewer. That is not your goal. Good companies don't hire candidates who make the interviewers happy. Instead, speak with your true voice. Make them think.

> If you get nervous before interviews, you're not alone. Take a breath between each sentence. This helps both psychologically and physiologically, and exudes confidence. It slows down your speech (people tend to talk fast when they're nervous), let's your mind and mouth catch up with one another, and allows the interviewer to really absorb what you're saying.
>
> **Kyle Elliot,** MPA, CHES (Career coach)

Chapter 8—What You Learned

How are your interviews going? Hopefully, at this point, you have had considerable practice interviewing. Remember—if at first you don't succeed, interview and interview again. We all have interviews that go south. It's ok. Consider it great practice for that opportunity around the corner. It will happen; it's just a matter of time.

Action Items:

- Ask others to perform mock interviews with you. You should do three mock interviews with three different people. Take notes! What did I do well? What do I need to work on?

- After your interviews, follow up.

- If you receive an opportunity to interview but don't think it matches your goals, go anyway. Its great practice, and you may be surprised by what they offer.

9

Accept an Offer

"Choose a job you love, and you will never have to work a day in your life."
–Confucius

After tons of work researching, networking, applying and interviewing, you have an offer. Good for you! You're understandably excited, but don't accept until you're ready. You need to think ahead. There's plenty to do:

Thank them.

Thank the hiring manager who made the offer, and state how excited you are before you do anything else. This sets a good tone moving forward. Using words like "excited" and "delighted" will get the point across...but don't accept the position yet.

Ask for the offer letter.

Once you've thanked the employer, request the offer letter. This is standard procedure. It should include the name of the position, a start date, a salary, and details about benefits. Receiving an offer letter makes it official, and gives you the chance to review it, to make sure you completely understand the offer. A responsible hiring manager should want prospective employees to have time to decide.

When accepting an offer, consider your duties—and the management style. Can you see yourself learning from their leadership? How did they get into the position, and what could you gain by working under them? Most importantly, can you see yourself taking their critical feedback, and will they support your professional goals?

Accept and sign graciously.

Finally, ask about the next steps. What paperwork is necessary? Will there be an orientation? How will you prepare for your first day?

Offer Negotiation

Even in the best of times, salary negotiation is a risky proposition for college graduates. In the majority of cases, starting salaries are set. You don't have enough to offer at this stage in your career to make employers budge. You can only negotiate if you have something special to negotiate with. A degree with a couple of internships isn't enough. Only when you have considerable experience or expertise can you really negotiate. Employers aren't going to pay extra for you to gain experience. Instead, focus on the experience you could gain and align it with your goals.

If, on the other hand, the hiring manager you're dealing with appears to be open to negotiations when it comes to your salary and other benefits (vacation, tuition reimbursement, relocation assistance, etc.), feel free to try it, but first, do your research. Ask for something reasonable, and avoid an attitude of entitlement. Be respectful.

Not only was the Puff Daddy single, "It's All About the Benjamins" my "jam" during the late '90s, these lyrics pretty much summed up my early career decision making. This all changed when, due to volatility in the industry that I was working (textiles and apparel) I was laid off. This unexpected career pause provided me the opportunity to more deeply reflect on both what I wanted to do next and, for the first time, what sort of work/organizational culture would enable my career satisfaction. For, as I was going through this exercise, gaps – often a function of an organization's culture – existed that both inhibited me realizing my potential within a given role and impacted, more importantly, my overall happiness.

The revelation that "Chasing the Benjamins" only masked what I was truly craving in a job became evident. While salary is important, fit, what I now understand, is equally of importance. A recent Fast Company article titled "This is the 3-step process you should follow when you get a job offer"(Kramer, 2018), challenges one to truly take a step back and ask oneself, what's the culture at this company, and how do I fit in?" And, answering this question is not as easy as I discovered.

What makes for a good fit can mean different things to different people, and the key to this understanding is identifying what is of value to you. The work environment, an organization's philosophy on work/life balance, and even available amenities, often drive compatibility and fit. Taking the time to do the necessary work to understand yourself better and what you need to be and bring your best self to the workplace to discern fit is critical.

While I hope that it does not take an unexpected event for you to begin this work, be proactive – pre-offer – and seek tools and support to self-assess. As you evaluate offers, leverage these insights in gauging fit. Don't underestimate its importance in accepting an offer – It's NOT just the Benjamins. Your job satisfaction and happiness can hinge on this understanding.

Woodrow W. Winchester, III, Ph.D., CPEM – Professor RMU

Chapter 9—What You Learned

Take your time when accepting an offer. Treat it carefully, and use your gut. Congratulations!

Action items:

- Take your time to reply to an offer. Use the templates in the back of the book to formulate an excellent email and accept when you are ready.
- Celebrate! You did it!

10

Create an Amazing Career

"The best way to predict the future is to create it."
−Abraham Lincoln

My best advice to new graduates: Find a way to make yourself valuable, no matter how small. When I first started in 2008, the economy was tanking, and I was last on the totem pole. I decided I needed to find a way to keep money coming into the company.

It turns out that we had a shortage of site supervisors. I wasn't qualified, but if I could convince the customer I was capable, I could keep money coming into the company...and my job. So, I flew to the job site and started site supervision. They ultimately decided that I was capable, and I ended up finishing the job successfully. I found a niche that would allow me to gain experience, stay employed, and most importantly, make myself more valuable.

Become Indispensable

What does it mean to be indispensable? Maybe you'll be the "go-to" person in the office. It can help you to make connections within the company, and it's great for your confidence. Managers will rely on you more, and that can increase your job security. Being indispensable means being irreplaceable. What are the steps to get there?

Be reliable.

Reliability is more than showing up to work and meetings on time. It's about following schedules, being efficient, and not giving up. Reliability also means addressing tasks you should be able to handle...and asking for help when you need it.

Become an expert...and share.

In any engineering firm, there are "hot" topics. These are the current issues around the industry in which your company is engaged or going after. Taking the opportunity to become an expert in these topics means you will be involved in some of the company's key priorities. When a task or job is related to the topic, you'll get it. Learning the skills required and becoming the expert will guarantee that you are indispensable at work. But make sure you are sharing this knowledge with others. You will add value to your company while positioning yourself as a leader on a topic.

Volunteer.

Volunteering for key projects can expose you to more opportunities. When you volunteer, make sure you have buy-in from your manager. For instance, volunteering for a project in purchasing—although it may relate to your job as a project engineer—may not be top on your manager's priority list. Volunteering for projects that are important to your manager will ensure he or she sees you as a go-getter and a valuable member of the organization.

Build relationships.

Building relationships with co-workers and customers will not only make you indispensable in your current position, but also lead to opportunities in the future. When it comes time for raises, the relationships may put you at the top of the list.

Offer solutions, not problems.

No one wants problems; everyone wants solutions. If you want to become indispensable, you need to find ways to solve problems. If you hear your colleagues complaining about an issue, figure out how to fix it. Think outside the box. You'll increase your value to your company as well as your manager. Eventually, you'll be approached to solve all kinds of problems...and in time, one of your solutions could mean a promotion to management.

Make your manager's job easier.

It allows them to concentrate on managerial duties. Having your manager on your side is very important. They are more likely to fight for you in a conflict, or even during layoffs. If you are completing tasks that your manager doesn't have time for, or even lacks the knowledge for, you are indispensable.

Think like an Engineer

Don't presume the solution. When it comes time to involve the designer in a project, assumptions have been made about the desired solution. A wise engineer investigates the problem and possible causes. The resulting discoveries may be different than anticipated, and possibly more effective.

Think systemically; a system must be analyzed thoroughly. A complete analysis is not the summation of its parts. The design of a component depends upon its relationship to the entire system and the behavior of the system. It can even correspond to other systems. Thinking systematically means analyzing consistently and thoroughly. It means considering the web of relationships within a system.

Few customers can afford to pay for a perfectly designed product! If a ten percent improvement costs $10, a twenty percent improvement will cost more than $20. Eventually, the cost of improving quality will outpace the improvement. The optimal quality-cost state occurs when the slopes of the value and the cost curves are equal.

There are designs within designs! A well-designed product really isn't well designed if:

- the manufacturing process is impossible;
- the equipment doesn't fit in its location;
- maintenance cannot access critical components;
- or if it's dangerous to operate or maintain.

The Business of Engineering

Having knowledge and passion for the business of engineering is essential to becoming an extraordinary engineer. Desire, however, is not enough. You need a basic understanding to help your organization prosper. You must have a basic knowledge of your company's operations, vision, planning, and finance.

Operations – How does your company's product make its way to the market? If you are a contractor or working for a contracting firm, it's possible that you are the product. How does your company use its people to the best of their abilities? What happens behind the scenes when your company launches a new product? Having a basic understanding of how your company produces its products can significantly help you optimize your processes in engineering. Is your product designed from the top down, but built from the bottom up? What is the production capacity of your facility? How is your productivity? How does your company conduct quality assurance?

Vision – You must understand clearly the strategic vision of your company. You must align your key decisions with the company's vision.

Finance – Do you understand basic finances? Can you read a financial statement? Do you understand budgets? A proper understanding of day-to-day accounting and finances is key to an engineering business. It's critical to operations. It's important to know how accounting can affect decision making. Your ability to read, analyze, and prepare financial statements is an essential skill if you plan to climb the ladder in an engineering firm.

Strategy – How does your company compete? What is your competitive advantage? How do you adapt to a changing market? The ability to take a wide-angle view of the landscape, changing customer demands, competition, and potential opportunities is a quality that great engineers possess. Think of Henry Ford. His ability to identify the market for automobiles, and creating the assembly line to increase production changed the course of American history.

Where can you learn core business skills? Consider your local community college, online courses, or an MBA. Business is a complicated animal; if you can learn the basics, you can start to tame the beast. You and your company will benefit from your advanced decision-making skills.

Young engineers must learn, in order to be successful, they have to start from the very bottom of the food chain. They must be humble but determined and complete tasks that few people want to do. Tasks that are repetitive, boring, and time-consuming are important and still need to be completed. They must respect others and learn how to create mutual trust and respect. Young engineers must have a flexible schedule, travel, take on additional responsibilities, work towards excellence, be proud to be recognized, and self-confident. A proper mental approach toward their work and colleagues will provide more chances of success than great technical skill.

Fabrizio Rambaldi, Director, Projects Services at Tenova Inc.

Focus on Solutions

Think in terms of solutions rather than focusing on problems. Often, we cannot immediately see the solution, but that does not mean that we will not find it. Listen to your subconscious to gain answers and ideas rather than to your inner voice saying that a goal is unachievable.

"Engineers love to solve problems. If there are no problems handily available, they will create their own problems."
−Scott Adams

Too often, when facing a problem, we tend to focus on a negative situation. We even repeat our dysfunctional patterns, repeating processes that do not work. Banish negative thoughts. Start searching for ways to resolve the situation by focusing on solutions. Don't react quickly; take the time to analyze the problem and possible solutions.

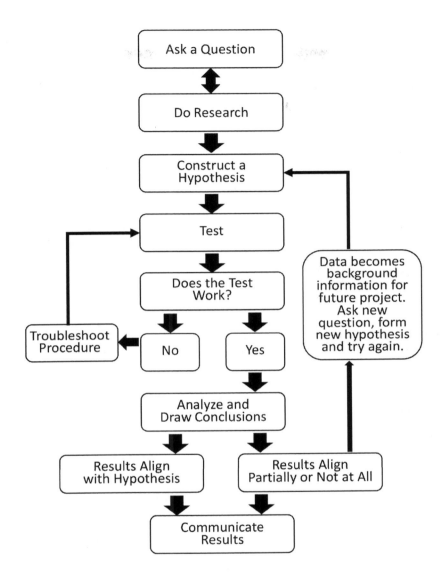

Regardless of how complicated your problem, there is a solution. You need to think long and hard enough to find it. When we start to think of alternative ways to overcome our problems, we can use the knowledge to overcome the situation at hand and prepare for the next challenge we will face. If we focus on problems, we will generate new problems. If we focus on solutions, we will get more solutions.

Engineering takes critical thinking and process analysis to solve the world's problems. Moving fluids, materials, electrical energy, chemicals, and the creation of each is the basis of engineering. A career in an engineering discipline has a high risk/ high reward relationship. In most cases, you give more than you receive and most contributions go unnoticed. But it's all worth it. What you get in return is worth much more than the sacrifice. A building designed to hold thousands of people exists because of sacrifices by engineers. Once you solve a complex problem, you can gaze at the spectacle of your creation and enjoy.

George Robinson II, Ph.D., MBA, Chemical and Environmental Engineer

Lifelong Learning

My number one secret to a successful engineering career is consistent personal improvement. It does not matter where you are in your career or what your position is. Learn all you can. In engineering, miracles do not happen. It's a consistent effort toward education that improves your career. Career success is the culmination of excessive learning and leveraging that knowledge to set and accomplish goals.

The term *lifelong learning* can be defined as "gathering valuable skills for your entire life." Skills should but don't have to relate to your profession. Lifelong learning can help you in many ways. It can improve your creativity, social skills, and even help you achieve a dream. Why not try it? Why not go back to school? Education doesn't have an age limit. If you have a vision that is outside of your skillset, go for it!

Often, a busy professional cannot enroll in full-time academics. Luckily, there are loads of alternatives. Many universities offer evening and online classes. The latter gives you a chance to benefit from programs that may be located far away. As an added benefit, online degrees tend to be more affordable.

Reading is possibly the simplest option for learning. You can learn about almost anything by reading. A novel may teach you creativity, while a non-fiction book can enlighten you on specific skills.

When people ask Elon Musk how he learned to build rockets, he has a simple answer.

"I read books."

Literature about your professional field will help you keep up with the latest trends and newest developments. It may also prevent you from repeating the past.

Learning isn't only about theory. You must practice your skills and use them to accomplish a goal. I keep myself involved in a few projects at once; for instance, I am a member of Toastmasters™, I mentor and coach young engineers, and I speak to university classes. These projects allow me to speak publicly, practice my leadership skills, and hone my knowledge of the experiences of young engineers. My goal? To learn as much as I can about my field, myself, and others.

Mentoring, volunteering, joining associations, and even serving on committees are all wonderful learning opportunities. Volunteering for cross-department projects at work is another great source. Dedicate time to something you enjoy doing, challenge yourself to complete a goal, and see what you are capable of achieving.

Don't stop learning. Sometimes we become so stuck in our current accomplishments that we fail to see how much the world changes around us. Let curiosity guide you. Embrace change. It will feel uncomfortable at first, but eventually, you'll understand the dynamic benefits that lifelong learning brings to our lives.

Build a Network

Why do we network? To create opportunities and make new connections. When you make new connections, you get the chance to display your skills and use others' skills to your advantage. Successful people network and create lasting relationships. Start by creating social media profiles on LinkedIn and Facebook. Get to know others who possess qualities and skills like yours. Ask questions. Most people relish the opportunity to talk about themselves. If you're willing to dedicate some free time and you're willing to get out of your comfort zone, networking will do great things for you. You never know when you may need to look for a job!

Facing Failure

Any engineer willing to pay the price can be successful. Remember, the difficult problems in engineering are the ones that help us develop. Anything that requires little effort and utilizes very few of our talents can hardly benefit us.

An estimated 5.3 million Americans have a social phobia; up to seventy four percent of people have speech anxiety, but only nineteen percent of people stated that they were afraid of death… which means that more people are afraid of public speaking than death. Public speaking fear also has a ten percent impairment in wages. (Gaille, 2017)

> *"Everything you want is on the other side of fear."*
> *—Jack Canfield*

Our fear of failure most likely started young. Perhaps yours started in grade school when you received an "F" on a test and you dreaded your parents' reactions, or even punishment. Maybe you played sports and hated being on the losing team. Whatever your circumstances, you learned very quickly that success is fun and failing is not.

It is not hard to understand why a fear of failure plagues many of us in adulthood. The stakes are much higher. Fear of failing at your marriage, fear of being a lousy parent, fear of losing your job or a promotion…this fear of failure applies to every significant milestone in life. What greater fear could there be than failing in your own life?

For some engineers, the fear of failure can cause a person to avoid anything that isn't safe. When confronted with a difficult situation, such as giving a presentation at work, they get overwhelmed. Taking risks is one of the only ways to get ahead in a career, but you need to take calculated risks.

Engineering culture loves innovation but hates failure. To be innovative, to invent something new, you risk punishment. Many people are not willing to try new things. When offered rewards for repeatedly trying new things, employees were more innovative and experienced more long-term success—even if their experiments failed (SIXWise, 2019). Traditional management styles leave employees too scared to try new things, so, in turn, they are less innovative.

Only by overcoming a fear of failure will you be able to succeed. Use these tips to focus on success and leave your fear of failure behind.

Expect failure.

When you do fail, embrace it.

Turn the failure into a positive by figuring out where you went wrong, then applying what you learned to your next endeavor.

Don't take failure personally; pick yourself up and try again.

Work-Life Balance

Managing all of your responsibilities is incredibly challenging. Your career, yourself, home, friends, and family all require your attention. You have a lot on your plate.

Not all aspects of a project need to be "engineered." I've heard the platitude "let's not reinvent the wheel" way too many times. Why? Because it's true. Identify your key project elements and focus the majority of your time on them. Leave the items that require little or no engineering for another time.

To save time, I look for ways to accomplish two things at one time. Best example: Do you have more than one project that has similar components? Design and purchase these at the same time. Getting quotes will be simpler and the purchasing department will save time as well.

Your free time doesn't have to be available time. In other words, if you are free Wednesday, it doesn't mean you have to accept when your friend asks you to attend an event. You can—and should—turn down invitations to make time for yourself.

When you lack free time, you can still do things you like. For instance, if you like sharing meals with your friends, try having coffee or lunch. If you like biking, try to hit the stationary bike at the gym. Use the free time you do have to experience a small version of what you love.

When I do get chunks of time to myself, I often feel obligated to get caught up on work or complete projects around the house. I've learned that I have to use the time to relax and do something for me. If I don't, I will burn myself out. I enjoy writing, wandering the library, going to the gym, woodworking, or just hitting a sports bar to watch a football game to get out of the usual daily duties. I strive to remind myself that time away from a computer screen is energizing and vital.

You can also schedule recurring social activities, or take a class at a local community college. By having regular events like this written into your calendar, you have something to look forward to that doesn't interfere with your evening responsibilities.

If you are like me, you continuously volunteer for more work. I've never had a boss that objects to me taking my work home, but I try my best not to. I have no problem staying and working late, or even getting up early in the morning and knocking out work before a morning meeting, but I rarely complete my work at home. When I leave the office, I leave my work for tomorrow. I make a clear separation between my work and my life away from work. It helps reduce my stress and keeps me from thinking about the complications of my projects.

Enjoy your weekends. Don't put off your chores to the end of the day on Sunday. Get them out of the way during the week or early on Saturday. That way, instead of spending your last few hours on Sunday night doing chores, you can fit something in that's fun and relaxing.

Carve out some time on the weekends, ideally a whole day, to stay away from screens. Shut your computer, phone, and TV off to do something physical or creative. Go for a bike ride. Consider paint or writing. Your mind will be more refreshed and a little sharper.

Loss of Motivation

Let's face it; not all parts of engineering are glorious. Often destruction defines our industry. When engineers create something that works, not many people care. When they create something that fails, no one forgets about it. Remember Joseph Bell, the engineer of the *Titanic*? Poor guy.

Processes and procedures can be overwhelming. When we go the extra mile, others can claim the credit, but when things go wrong, the blame is ours. What drives us on those days? What propels you forward, so that each year is full of growth and development?

Motivation is the key to keep you moving each day. If you are not motivated, you tend to procrastinate. You will put things off... and eventually give up on your dreams. This happens to many young engineers. They say they want to land a position with a top engineering firm, but fail to research, network, or build a rapport. They don't have a clear path to their dreams, they get overwhelmed, and they lose motivation. Unfortunately, it's all too common.

Below are seven great ways to overcome a loss of motivation:

Remember why you chose engineering.

The question "why" is the driving force behind everything you do. It is only when your "why" is strong and emotional enough that you will do whatever it takes to accomplish the task.

Why do you love engineering? Why do you want to achieve your goals? Make sure your reasons are strong and emotional. When you feel no motivation, think about the reason why you've spent so much time and money on your career.

Envision success.

Does visualization work? Yes, but only if you are willing to work on it. Visualization is a powerful tool. Think about all of the commercials during a football game. There's pizza, chicken wings, subs, and beer. The ads can make you salivate by showing you delicious melted cheese, or cold brewed beer pouring into a tall glass. These emotions come to you when you experience a strong vision.

When you imagine and visualize things in your mind, you will feel motivated toward them. When you dream about the career you want, you will create the motivation from within. Next time you feel a lack of motivation, try visualizing your success.

Find support.

We act like the people around us. It's a natural tendency that happens to all of us. Surrounding yourself with others that are upbeat, friendly, and want the best for you can have a positive impact on your mood. If you are in a slump, these people can keep you motivated. Opening yourself up around friends and family can help you to overcome a difficult situation and boost your mood. Your surroundings are important. Change them instead of letting them change you.

Exercise.

When you exercise, your brain releases endorphins, serotonin, and dopamine. They, in turn, make you feel better. After exercising, you may feel a sense of accomplishment, and your muscles will relax because of the workout. This can ease tension, stress, and allow you to get back on track.

Entertainment.

Listening to music or watching your favorite movie can motivate you. I dare you—try watching *Good Will Hunting* without feeling as if you can conquer the world.

Find things in your life that can kick start your mindset on those tough days. When you are down, try to watch something inspiring, like YouTube or a motivational TEDx speech.

Dream big, but take small steps.

When you dream, dream big. Big enough so that when you visualize the effects, it energizes you. Start small. This way you can take action consistently, and every day. When I decided to take the P.E. exam, my first step was to make a list of all the related expenses: course registration, books, application fees, exam fees, and finally my stamp.

My next step was to approach management to try and get funding. My goal was large, but my day-to-day activities were small. Receiving my books, studying chapter-by-chapter, watching lectures, and taking notes all added to my progress. Commit to the small steps, and before you know it, you are halfway there.

Take a break.

On a stressful day, I like to take a break for a few minutes and think. I think of the moments when I have used my engineering expertise and experience to help others. I think of the successes within my career and how much impact I have had for my customers. I think about the help I was able to give other engineers and the opportunities they may not have had otherwise. I think about the ways I handled those issues and how far I've come over the years.

Career success is not a destination; it's a journey that takes time... much more time than you may have considered. Some engineers lose their motivation and give up on their goals too early. Don't let this happen to you. Successful engineers are diligent. They are persistent and never give up. Real success takes time. Take action consistently, and when you need a break, take it. Greatness, like beauty, requires sleep.

I get out of bed every morning to see what's next. I get excited about the possibilities, the learning opportunities, and becoming a better engineer. I believe in what I'm doing. Find something you can believe in.

How to Ruin Your Career

Your professional reputation can take years, even decades, to build. But it can be tarnished easily, and difficult to salvage. Follow my list below to avoid a career derailment.

Don't:

Back out of a new job.

Once you decide to accept a position, stick with it. Keep your word. If you burn that bridge, your employer will chat about you within their—and your—industry. Be sure to conduct yourself with the highest professionalism.

Quit without giving notice.

When you leave a job without two weeks' notice, you're burning the bridge. Always give your employer a heads-up. By leaving smoothly, on good terms, you increase your likelihood of a positive reference.

Focus on problems without solutions.

You're an engineer. Your job is to solve problems. Often those problems are not to calculate this or design that; they are to figure out how much does this cost and how soon can we get that. If you are an engineer that consistently complains and you dedicate your time to being the "devil's advocate," your co-workers and even your boss are going to get frustrated. Everyone has different problems to solve. You need to put effort toward solving yours.

Ignore emails, calls, or meetings.

Things happen. We all get busy, but if you are someone who doesn't respond to emails, ignores calls, or skips meetings when people are counting on you, they will stop relying on you. Be an asset, not a nuisance.

Resist change.

Never say never and keep an open mind. How long can a business last if it doesn't change? How long will you last if you don't change? A "We've always done it this way" mentality will only get you so far. You must embrace new ideas and perspectives to keep from descending into nothingness.

Over-promise…and under-deliver.

If you can't walk the walk, don't talk the talk. Don't make promises you can't keep. Manage your time well and turn in your work on or ahead of time. If you feel overwhelmed or may not be able to complete a task on schedule, speak up. Keep communications open and make sure you and your manager are on the same page.

Make excuses.

Don't play the victim. It gets old fast. It is not anyone else's fault you missed the mark. Be a problem solver, not the problem. Learn from your mistakes, and take responsibility for your failures.

Lie.

Honesty is a fundamental characteristic that always has value. When you make a mistake, own up to it. Getting caught in a lie is much worse than admitting you are wrong. Your boss would much rather hear you own up to a mistake than try to cover it up. The cover-up always makes a problem worse.

Send an angry email.

You are upset, and you want to send an angry email to tell off a co-worker who wronged you. You want to let everyone know what happened. In reality, you're coming off as immature and reckless. No one wants to work with those people. Cool off before you hit the send button.

If necessary, write out some of the angry thoughts to yourself and revisit them later. If you still think they are valid, figure out your next steps. Ideally, you will reread them and find a better way to handle the situation.

11

Continue Your Education

"If there are no stupid questions, then what questions do stupid people ask? Do they get smart just in time to ask questions?"
—Scott Adams

Career development is the accumulation and cultivation of skills and knowledge that enable a professional to advance or grow in the field of their choice. This can take the form of academic courses, professional certification, training, or on-the-job experience. In the field of mechanical engineering, one of the keys to career development is certification, a portable and concrete representation of the fact that an individual has achieved a certain skill level.

Ask your company for assistance. They will appreciate your effort to continue your education—and may pay for you to do so. It's well worth the conversation, and often companies have allocated money for their employees' continued education.

There are hundreds of courses, certifications, and licenses that an engineer can obtain to advance their education and career. The important aspects to consider when looking for a class, certification, or licensure are:

- Does it align with my career goals?
- Does it align with an opportunity?
- Young engineers often spend valuable time and money on a course or certification without determining its relevance. Below are the most typical—and in my opinion, the most important—certifications/licenses that an engineer can obtain:
- Fundamentals of Engineering (F.E.) exam
- Professional Engineering (P.E.) exam
- Project Management Professional (P.M.P.)
- LEED Certification
- Lean Six Sigma

When I first entered the workforce as an engineer with General Electric, I had the opportunity to participate in the Corporate Technical Leadership Program. As a part of this program, in addition to my "day job," I also had other responsibilities in the form of both internal and external training experiences.

GE's role in continuing my education in my first years in the workforce included Advanced Course training on fundamentals of engineering, communication and leadership training, project management training, and product line training. In addition, GE sent me to a local university to pursue a Master's degree in Mechanical Engineering. The master's degree program took about two years to complete on a part-time basis and also included preparing a master's thesis. While proving to be a great deal of work, the experience of advanced coursework, time management, and managing a project was tremendously beneficial.

As a young and confident engineer, I still remember a mentor of mine explaining the nature of engineering degrees. An engineer with a bachelor's degree knows everything about everything. Thus my confidence! An engineer with a master's degree realizes that we know a lot about some things. An engineer with a Ph.D., on the other hand, has discovered that we don't know anything about anything!

This is why the master's degree is said to be the most marketable engineering degree. It strikes the desired balance of breadth and depth of knowledge. It also reflects on your interest in improving your abilities in the field, to personal development, to achieve a goal that requires a long-term effort. I am certain that my engineering master's degree played a role in my subsequent career moves.

Admittedly, though I love my "day job" of working in engineering, underneath it all, I am an academic at heart. So, shortly after completing my master's degree, I enrolled in an evening MBA program. Taking a couple of classes each semester, it took me three years to complete the program. As an engineer, with a solid understanding of math and logical relationships,

I found many MBA classes to be fairly easy, requiring only a modest amount of preparation for exams. This was the case in Accounting, Finance, and Quantitative Decision Making. But, other classes, such as Strategic Planning and Marketing, I found the experience to be more challenging, and frankly, more beneficial.

I know that an MBA is also a valued degree in certain areas. I also recognize that not everybody has the same career goals. So, an MBA is not right for everybody. But for me, I found that it greatly improved my ability to understand the underlying business aspects of working for a company. It was also helpful in my engineering job, from presenting investment justifications, promoting company products and technologies, and developing and evaluating strategies for the company.

Needless to say, I have come to utilize the tools I gained in the MBA program, and have incorporated them into my engineering career. Like with the engineering master's degree, the MBA played in a role in my career advancement. I was able to leverage it in my progression into management roles.

So, do I recommend continuing education for engineers? You could say that!

Continuing education has been something that I have put a great value on. I have made personal educational investments in both time and money. And, I think that the payback (improved job performance, mental satisfaction, personal enjoyment, and yes, financial too!) has been there to support my decisions.

Jared Kaufman, P.E., M.S., MBA Vice President, Technical Services

Fundamentals of Engineering (F.E.) Exam

One of the most essential certifications an engineer can obtain is the Engineer-in-Training (E.I.T.) certificate by passing the Fundamentals of Engineering (F.E.) exam. The F.E. is the first step in earning your P.E. (Professional Engineer) license. To perform consulting work, work for the government, or stamp critical engineering documents, you will have to first pass the F.E. and then the P.E. to become a registered, licensed engineer. Each state has its licensing requirements, including the F.E. and P.E., in order to protect the safety, health, welfare, and property of its people.

The P.E. is similar to a driver's license. It is unlawful to drive a car on a public road without a license. Similarly, it is illegal to work in the form of engineering consultation, investigation, evaluation, or design without a P.E. license. The E.I.T. license, therefore, is the "driver's permit" that allows you to study under a P.E. as part of the licensure requirements.

The F.E. is open to anyone with a degree in engineering, related field, or currently enrolled in the last year of an ABET-accredited engineering degree program. Some states permit students to take the exam before their final year, and numerous states allow those without approved degrees to take the exam if they have the number of years of work experience in engineering that matches the state guidelines; the state of Michigan has no admission pre-requisites for the F.E.

You can take the exam no more than three times per 12-month period; it is managed by the National Council of Examiners for Engineering and Surveying (NCEES): **www.ncees.org**.

What if my field doesn't require a P.E.?

Take it anyway. Seriously! Often young engineers do not know if they need to take the P.E. exam. I didn't realize the importance until a few years into my career. Since the F.E. Exam is the prerequisite to the P.E., why not pass it now, obtain the certificate, and then make the decision to take the P.E. later on? It is much easier to pass when you have all of the subjects fresh in your mind from school. The longer you wait, the harder it becomes.

How much does it cost?

At the time of this writing, the exam costs $225, payable to NCEES. It does not include any supplies needed to prepare for the exam (e.g., review materials, calculator). If you reschedule after enrolling, NCEES will charge an additional $50.

What is the format of the exam?

The exam is computer-based and contains 110 multiple-choice questions; you will have 5 hours and 20 minutes to complete the exam.

The exam is divided into two parts, 50-60 questions each. However, the exam time is not divided into half. It is up to you how much time you use in the first half of the exam. If you complete the first half of the exam in 2 hours and 20 minutes, you will have 3 hours to complete the second half. Be careful not to use all of your time in the first half of the exam.

Exam topics are self-contained in each section. In other words, if you have thermodynamics questions in the first half, you will not have those type of problems in the second half. Similarly, if you do not have any economics questions in the first half, expect to see them in the second half.

Most importantly, the exam does not penalize you for incorrect answers. Even if you are unsure how to solve a question, GUESS ANYWAY! The worst thing that you can do is to leave a question blank.

What study materials should I use and where can I get them?

F.E. Reference Handbook – This is available through the NCEES website—it costs $14 for a paper copy, but it is FREE to download as a PDF to your computer. It is a comprehensive resource of key formulas and topics to assist you during the exam. It is provided to you at the exam as a split-screen next to the exam questions. Thus, it is critical to familiarize yourself with what formulas are and are not included, and where they are located.

F.E. Practice Exam – This is available through the NCEES website—each exam costs $30 and is computer-based, like the actual exam. It contains half as many questions as the real exam, but it is a great way to prepare.

F.E. Review Manual & F.E. Practice Problems – Michael Lindeburg, a P.E. himself, has published many resources for those studying for the F.E. in each discipline. The review manual contains abridged lessons of major engineering topics that are tested on the exam, along with selected sample problems; the practice problem book contains significantly more sample problems that complement the topics in the review manual. Both books are readily available on Amazon—the review manual being roughly $200, and the practice problem book around $40. If you are still a student, contact your college's library, as they may already have these books for borrowing. If not, your local library may be able to either purchase them, or obtain them via an interlibrary loan. Once you pass, you will no longer need these books. Why not save the money?

What can I bring to the exam (e.g., calculator)? What is provided?

The exam center provides a laminated notepad and a marker for performing hand calculations and scratch work. There is a basic calculator on the exam computer, but the testing center allows you to bring an approved calculator.

The best calculator is the TI 36X Pro Engineering/Scientific Calculator. It is the most useful calculator that an engineer can have that is not a graphing calculator. It can perform trig functions, definite integrals, numerical derivatives, and many other helpful capabilities. It very affordable on Amazon—about $15. You will need it for the P.E. exam. Get familiar with it.

NCEES allows the following calculators for the F.E. exam:

- Casio fx-115 and fx-991 (all models)
- Hewlett-Packard HP 33s and HP 35s
- Texas Instruments TI-30X and TI-36X (all models)

How long should I study?

This exam is not to be taken lightly. Do not expect to pass by allotting yourself only two weeks or even one month to study. Set aside at least 3-4 months of preparation time before the exam. Do not study the night before the exam. Rest—it will be a long day.

Is it difficult?

This is a question relative to the individual. If you prepare well, and take the exam and preparations seriously, the exam should be relatively straightforward. The goal of the exam is to test you on general concepts that any undergraduate engineer should know. There are no trick questions. All questions take between 10 seconds and 3 minutes to complete.

From a personal viewpoint, on a scale of 1-10, ten being extremely difficult, upon sufficient studying and preparation, I rate the exam about a three. The tricky part is the wide variety of questions.

How do I sign up?

https://ncees.org/exams/examinee-guide/

Professional Engineering (P.E.) Exam

Is a Professional Engineering license worth it? You're busy, and it's expensive. Will it make sense for you and your family?" Are the "P.E." initials after your name worth the time and effort?

Yes, yes, and yes. It is! Here are my five reasons why:

Career development – Your employer will treat engineers who have their P.E. license differently. It shows your commitment to your career and demonstrates your abilities as an engineer. Many engineering firms only have licensed engineers as engineering managers. The P.E. is also proof of your ability to provide services directly to the public. Having the designation of P.E. after your name is a career advantage that will last the rest of your life. What do you see in your career path? A P.E. should be at the top of the list!

Job security – A P.E. will set you apart from a crowd. Out of 100 job applicants, if ten have their P.E., which applicants do you think will get interviews? I am guessing five or six of the candidates that have their P.E. During the hiring process, a P.E. shows that the engineer has met the national standards—and this sets them apart from others. The more the engineering field grows, the more valuable you will be. If you have a P.E., think of all the opportunities you could find throughout a 40-year career. A license opens up career opportunities for growth and leadership.

Respect – As a P.E., you are respected in your field like other licensed professionals. It is like being part of an elite group. Your peers, community, managers, even customers, will hold you in higher esteem. A license is an important distinction that can enhance your career. When I received my P.E., I posted those two letters on everything—email signatures, business cards, LinkedIn, even Facebook. I wanted the world to know what I had accomplished.

> *"Basically, being a P.E. means that you are at the top of your game, top of your profession. They don't just hand that out to anybody."*
> *–Randal E. Riebel, P.E.*

Authority – Only a P.E. can stamp engineering drawings. For consultants, structural engineers, and private practice, many government agencies require licensure for their engineers. It is required by law for those who are designing to be responsible for their work. If you want to start your own business, licensure is a legal requirement.

Money – A P.E. tends to earn more than their non-licensed counterparts do. It pays to be in a position to compete with others who have a P.E. license. The more roles you can fill, the more you are worth.

According to The Engineering Income and Salary Survey published in 2012, the median salary for a full-time, salaried, licensed Professional Engineer was $100,000. The highest full-time salaried median income by a major branch of engineering goes to those working in ocean

($169,000), minerals and metals ($121,000), fire protection ($116,000), and electrical ($115,200) engineering. (Erway, 2014)

How do I pass the P.E.?

First off, let me say that if you are considering or already enrolled to take the P.E. exam, good for you. It will help your career tremendously. Your potential for advancement will increase, and you will find avenues for career growth you never considered before.

To pass the P.E. exam, I went to Professional Publications Inc. (PPI2Pass.com) for their 18-week preparation course. The course is offered online and live, and it also allows you to view the recordings later. I watched each recording repeatedly.

Plan, plan, and plan some more. Nothing will help you more on the P.E. exam than having a solid plan. Lay it out on paper and follow through. This will ensure your preparations are complete. This is another reason why the PPI course is so valuable. They do the planning for you with their weekly lectures and homework assignments.

I completed every portion of the course. The course guarantees that if you follow all the guidelines but do not pass the exam, you can retake the course for free. I made sure I followed all the guidelines to be sure I was adequately prepared to pass or to retake the class.

This is what I took with me for the Mechanical – Thermal and Fluids exam:

- PPI mechanical reference manual
- PPI practice problems book
- PPI quick reference guide
- PPI unit conversions book
- Notes and homework from the PPI course
- Copy of the FE reference manual
- Heat transfer book (depends on which exam you're taking).
- Mollier diagrams 11×17 (depends on which exam you are taking)

Tab your reference manual, guides, and notes diligently. I had labeled/color-coded tabs at each section that I used on the PPI homework. I even pasted equations directly in the reference book in the correct section. If I rearranged an equation to complete a homework assignment, I wrote it in the reference book. I highlighted and tabbed any conversion factors I used during my preparation in the PPI unit conversions book. My ability to quickly find the correct information and equations was critical to completing the exam on time.

Bring what you know. I noticed many students hauled in a ton of books to the exam. When I spoke to them after the test, they said they did not use many of them. The simpler, the better. Bring what you know and nothing you don't. You don't have time to rifle through a bunch of books to find the right equation. You need to have the information readily at hand.

Prepare for the worst. Show up early and know where you are going. I arrived at the testing site the day before the exam. I checked into a hotel and walked the path to the exam location the night before. Being able to visualize the route in the morning gave my brain some relief.

Do not study the night before the exam. This may sound counterintuitive, but the test is 8 hours long. Your brain needs a good night's rest before the big day. If you are not as prepared as you should be the night before the exam, a few hours of studying aren't going to help you anyway.

Always guess. If you do not pick a solution, you will always get the question wrong. I don't recommend giving a pure guess; I would try your best to eliminate an answer or two and then guess from there.

If you prepare accordingly, the test will be easier than you thought. I had an enormous amount of anxiety before the exam. I couldn't concentrate on anything but the exam for weeks prior; I even found myself making wrong turns on the way home from work. What I found was that the test was easier than I anticipated. I think I over- prepared, but I wouldn't do it any other way. When I finished the test, I had all the confidence that I had passed…and sure enough, I did.

For more P.E. exam advice, visit:

https://ppi2pass.com/pe-exam/resources/pe-exam-advice

Project Management Professional (P.M.P.)

A P.M.P. is for those engineers that would like to gain knowledge and certification in project management. It was created by the Project Management Institute (PMI®), a non-profit organization whose goal is to advance the profession of project management.

Education requirements – A four-year degree (bachelor's or the global equivalent), and at least three years of project management experience (4,500 hours leading and directing projects, and 35 hours of project management education); or a high school diploma with 7,500 hours leading and directing projects. Experience may NOT go back for more than eight years, and cannot be overlapping.

You will need to send PMI® the details of your experience and education, so it's best to gather and prepare this information before you open the application. Otherwise, it will likely take you multiple sessions to complete. Once you open an application, it will remain active for 90 days, after which time it will close.

Once you've determined that you meet the eligibility criteria, it's time to apply. Collect the following information, and then use the PMI® website to guide you through the process:

- Contact information—email, address, phone number.
- Education attained—school attended, level of education attained, degree date.
- Domain experience—details of the projects, programs, portfolios you've worked on, including qualifying hours, dates of employment, role, organization details, reference, and experience summary. Be sure to include specific project details, and use terminology from the PMBOK (Project Management

Book of Knowledge). Your overall experiences must cover ALL five process groups (initiating, planning, executing, monitoring and controlling, and closing).

- Domain education—names of courses completed, institutions attended, dates, qualifying hours.

Once PMI® receives your application, they will verify that you meet the eligibility criteria, and that your experience and education are valid and consistent with the guidelines stated in the certification handbook. Typically, the application review period will take 5–10 days, depending on the certification.

Tip: Join PMI®, as it will save you money on the exam fee, Professional Development Units (continuing education), give you access to a wide range of products and knowledge, and also provide you with opportunities to network in the project management world.

What to expect – Two hundred total questions, twenty-five of which are "experimental." These questions are used by PMI® to create future tests and are not considered in your test score. You will not know which questions are experimental and which are not. It is a computer-based exam, and you will not be given a score or a numeric result. Immediately upon completion, you will receive a pass or fail.

Most questions are based on information directly out of the PMBOK. However, the exam may also contain questions related to "common" project management knowledge and processes that are not included in the PMBOK. A good exam prep course (see below) will cover this information.

Study! Consider enrolling in an exam prep course and forming a study group with your colleagues or friends.

The P.M.P. exam is more about your knowledge of the PMI® project management process—domains, process groups, and ITTOs (inputs, tools, techniques, and outputs)—than it is about how effectively you can manage a project. Success on the exam is largely based on memorization of this information, but the exam will also expect you to be able to apply this information to real-world scenarios. The exam is also a test of your test-taking ability. In other words, you must read the questions VERY carefully to understand. Often, questions will be asked in such a way to trick you into thinking it is about one topic, when in fact it is about another.

A good P.M.P. exam prep course will explain this in great detail and provide numerous sample questions, as well as a sample test, to help you get accustomed to the types of questions that will be on the test. I highly recommend taking one of these courses, regardless of other forms of study that you are planning to do.

Understanding your exam results – An overall pass/fail result is generated based on the number of questions you answered correctly.

You will also receive a proficiency assignment for each project management domain (initiation, planning, executing, monitoring and controlling, and closing). There are three levels of proficiency: proficient, moderately proficient, and below proficient.

PMI® defines three levels of proficiency as follows:

- Proficient – indicates performance is above the average level of knowledge in this domain.

- Moderately Proficient – indicates performance that is at the average level of knowledge in this domain.

- Below Proficient – indicates performance is below the average level of knowledge in this domain.

(Singh, 2017)

For more information go to **www.pmi.org**

LEED Certification

LEED stands for Leadership in Energy and Environmental Design. It is a popular green building certification developed by a non-profit organization—the U.S. Green Building Council (USGBC)—and used worldwide as a green building certification. The USGBC uses a rating system for the design, operation, construction, and maintenance of commercial buildings, homes, and neighborhoods. The program helps building owners and operators to be environmentally friendly and use resources more responsibly.

In the U.S., buildings account for:

- 38% of all CO2 emissions;
- 13.6% of all potable water usage (15 trillion gals. /year);
- and 73% of electricity consumption.

LEED projects are responsible for diverting over 80 million tons of waste from landfills. Compared to the average commercial building, LEED Gold buildings in the General Services Administration's portfolio consume twenty five percent less energy and generate thirty four percent less greenhouse gas emissions.

More than 79,000 projects are participating in LEED across 160 countries and territories, comprising over 15 billion square feet. USGBC estimates that nearly 5 million people experience a LEED building every day. Many of the world's most well-known buildings have earned LEED certification.

How It Works:

LEED projects earn points across nine basic areas that address key aspects of green buildings:

- Integrative process
- Location and transportation
- Sustainable sites
- Water efficiency
- Energy and atmosphere (Council, 2019)
- Materials and resources
- Indoor environmental quality
- Innovation
- Regional priority

The benefits of LEED Buildings:

- Provide a competitive differentiator
- Make for happier employees and occupants

- Attract tenants
- Save energy and resources, lower operating costs
- Are cost effective
- Provide public relations with community benefits
- Increase rental rates
- Optimize health

For a building project to earn LEED Certification, it must meet certain criteria and goals within the following categories:

- Location and Transportation – How close the project is to mass transit.
- Materials and Resources – Uses locally sourced, sustainable products.
- Water Efficiency – Reduces potable water usage.
- Energy and Atmosphere – Improves energy performance and indoor air quality.
- Sustainable Sites – Utilizes nearby natural resources and ecosystems that can naturally take part in the design, minimizing environmental pollution.
- Regional Priority Credits – Addresses a particular concern based on location.
- Innovation – Any idea not covered under the main LEED areas. (Training, 2018)

According to **http://leed.usgbc.org/leed.html**, several types of credential levels and over 201,000 individuals have earned the following:

LEED Accredited Professional – Affirms advanced knowledge in green building and expertise in a particular LEED rating system. The LEED AP is available with a variety of specialties for professionals to demonstrate proficiency in certain building types.

LEED Green Associate – Demonstrates a solid and current foundation in green building principles and practices.

LEED Fellow – A peer-nominated designation awarded to highly accomplished individuals with ten or more years of professional green building experience.

The following is required to gain the LEED credentials:

- Proper experience
- Written letter for exam approval
- Pass the LEED exam

For more information on credentials visit:
http://greenworkexperience.com/leed-ap-exam-requirements

Lean Six Sigma

Lean Six Sigma is a methodology that relies on a collaborative team effort to improve performance by systematically removing waste and reducing variation. It combines lean manufacturing/lean enterprise and Six Sigma to eliminate the eight kinds of waste:

- Defects
- Over-Production
- Waiting
- Non-Utilized Talent
- Transportation
- Inventory
- Motion
- Extra-Processing

Lean Six Sigma not only reduces process defects and waste, but also provides a framework for overall organizational culture change.

Mr. Fujio Cho of Toyota defines waste as "anything other than the minimum amount of equipment, materials, parts, space, and workers time which are essential to add value to the product."

As mentioned above, there are different types of waste. They are defined below:

Overproduction is an excess amount of product that is produced. Idle time waste, or wait time waste, is downtime that is spent waiting for a product to be created. The delivery waste, or transportation waste, is the time spent getting the product shipped to the recipient. Waste in the work, inventory, and operations is time spent loosely and does not make money.

12

Conclusion

At the beginning of this book, I told you about the investment of education, how your grades don't matter as much as you may think they do, myths about engineers, what they do, and what it takes to be a great engineer.

Although the road to becoming a great engineer may be a challenging one, I promise you that it's filled with vast fulfillment and personal reward. The thrill of seeing your engineering talents put to use is something extraordinary. You will surprise yourself with your accomplishments.

I have provided you with many valuable tools and real-world resources. I hope that you study them and use them to start building your own successful career. There are also many helpful articles at **www.engineeryourcareer.net**.

Too many engineers go to the web to find a job…but if that is your method, your chances of landing a position that fits your purpose are slim to none. Job searches on the internet are fraught with fierce competition, ATS software, and fake job posts. If you do decide to apply online, do so to the best of your ability, move on, and don't let the lack of responses get you down. Don't doubt your abilities based on the number of responses you do—or don't—receive.

Networking is key. Engineering clubs, societies, and organizations are looking for members just like you. Without membership, those organizations would not be around for long. They offer huge discounts to young members, and provide perfect networking opportunities. Contact them. They want to talk to you, and you need to meet their members. I have met the most amazing people in engineering by networking.

Fortune favors the brave. Find what you want. Go out, get bold, and land the engineering career of your dreams.

13

Templates

Here are the templates that can help you along the way. If you would like the native files, you can download them for free at: www.engineeryourcareer.net/templates

Cover Letter

ADDRESS
PHONE
EMAIL
LINKEDIN

Mr. [Name Here]
[Title]
[Company or University]
[Address]

Dear Mr. [Name Here];

My professionalism, personal accountability, and motivation can provide immense value to [Company] and your customers. My technical skills, problem-solving, and attention to detail can add significant value to your team.

As noted in my résumé, I offer [Company] strong industry experience and exceptional results. My [# years] of experience have allowed me to utilize and sharpen my abilities. Listed below are some of my best attributes and accomplishments:

- Maintain a professional, respectful, and friendly attitude both in and out of the office. Have a strong sense of ownership and personal accountability.
- Have a strong work ethic. Work beyond my duties and work closely with other groups to improve the final products.

Based on my education, training, hands-on experience, and acquired skills, I am confident that I will be able to provide an immediate contribution to your customers, projects, and teams.

I will contact your office in the coming week to follow up on my résumé submission. If you have any questions before then, please call or email me. Thank you in advance for your consideration.

–Your first and last name
–Signature

Interested in a Job Email

Hello, Mr. / Ms. [Last name];

I am reaching out because I saw the posting for [Job Title] at [Company]. After I researched the position and company, I am confident I would be a great fit for the opportunity.

I possess the required skills and believe I will integrate well with the culture at [Company]. In particular, I like how the company [something notable from your research; for instance, "believes in advancing new technology to help people live healthier lives"]. [Give an example of why your skills are a good cultural fit; for instance, "I am proficient with AutoCAD Inventor, and I have experience working with teams. I know that's important to the company's operation."]

Note: If the job description lists skills or experience you do not have, you will gain credibility by addressing them. "I noted the job description requires experience with CFD. While I do not have that direct experience, I was selected to lead the implementation of a Finite Element Analysis and kept the project on time and under budget."

I have attached my résumé. I am open to your feedback on my candidacy and overall portfolio.

Note: Ask for feedback, because it allows the hiring manager to engage in dialogue. It may help you build trust within your relationship.

Thanks, and I hope to hear from you.

–Your first and last name
–Email signature

Job Search Letter/Email

Contact Name
Title
Company
Address
City, State Zip Code

Dear Mr. / Ms. [Last name];

[Name] from [Company] referred me to you, and recommended you as an excellent source of information for engineering opportunities.

My goal is to secure an entry-level position in engineering. I would appreciate hearing your advice on career opportunities in the engineering industry, on conducting an effective job search, and on how best to uncover job leads.

Thanks so much, in advance, for any insight and advice you would be willing to share. I look forward to contacting you early next week to set up an informational telephone interview. To respect your time, I will keep the conversation to less than 30 minutes. Thank you for your consideration.

Sincerely,

–Your first and last name
–Email signature

Email about a Job

Subject line examples:

- Junior Engineer Application
- John Smith Following up on Engineering Position
- John Smith for Electrical Engineering Position
- Mechanical Engineer—John Smith, EIT
- Referred by Jane Brown for Chemical Engineering Position

Hello, Mr. / Ms. [Last name];

My name is [your name] and I found your post for a [Role Title] up on [website/job board + link to posting], and I wanted to share my cover letter and résumé with you.

I have an excellent foundation for working in/with [relevant tools]. I'm looking forward to helping [Company] deliver even more unique value to the [industry].

My experience in [engineering discipline, or specialty] with [relevant experience] will make an excellent addition to your team.

Let me know when you have a moment to chat this week.

Thank you,

–Your first and last name
–Email signature

Follow-Up Email about a Job

If you would like to follow up for a potential job opportunity, send an email within a day to keep them in your mind.

Subject line: Follow-up from [location]

Hello again, Mr. / Ms. [Last name];

It was great to meet you on [day you met] at the [location or event]. I enjoyed our conversation about [mention a part of the conversation]. After our discussion, I did some research on [Company]. I am interested in discussing more about [Company] and projects like [name, if applicable. Mention why you like the project].

As I mentioned at [location or event], I am a [engineering education and experience as it relates to the project/company you're interested in].

Please let me know if you can pass my résumé on to the appropriate person, or if you prefer to give me a contact, I can handle the introduction myself.

Thank you,

–Your first and last name
–Email signature

Note: Depending on the person, you may want to ask for a call to receive feedback on your résumé before passing on.

Email about an Internship

Subject line examples:

- Engineering Internship Application
- John Smith Following up on Internship
- John Smith for Electrical Engineering Internship
- Mechanical Engineering Intern—John Smith

Hello, Mr. / Ms. [Last name];

My name is [your name] and I am a [freshman, sophomore, etc.] at [university]. I hope you are doing well.

I see that [Company] offers internships, and I want to learn more about the application process.

I am interested in [___ engineering] and hope to gain real world experience with your team. (A sentence on what you like about the company].

Note: Give a few more sentences that make you look appealing. For instance: I was on the volleyball team, student government, and the student chapter of ___. I am a dependable person and I look forward to helping [Company] any way I can as an intern.

I have attached my résumé; let me know if I can provide any more information.

Thanks so much, and I look forward to hearing from you.

–Your first and last name
–Email signature

Thank You Letter/Email

Note: If you have had an interview, it is best to send a note the same day. If you have traveled to the location, make sure you send the note within 24 hours.

Subject line: Thank you for the interview

Hello again, Mr. / Ms. [Last name];

Thank you again for meeting me [today or yesterday]. I enjoyed our conversations, appreciated your time, and look forward to learning more about [Company].

    Note: Include couple of lines from your conversation about why you would be good for the company. Example: "As we discussed, I am interested in a _____ position. I feel that my skills would be a nice complement to your engineering department."

    If you have any further questions, feel free to ask. Thank you, and [reference one of your conversations. Example: "have a good time at the baseball game"].

–Your first and last name
–Email signature

Offer Negotiation Letter

Subject: [Your name] – My thoughts on [person]'s offer

Hello again, Mr. / Ms. [Last name];

[Company] seems like a great company, and this particular opportunity is an exciting one for me; I'm a great fit for [Company]'s needs, and it's an excellent chance for me to continue growing as an (a) _____ engineer.

Thank you for extending an offer. It is somewhat disappointing, as it seems to be a bit below what I've seen for similar jobs in my market research. This is an exciting opportunity, but I want to be sure that this move is a step forward in my career.

Are there improvements that can be made to this offer so I can consider them?

Thank you for your time!

–Your first and last name
–Email signature

Offer Acceptance

Subject: [Your name] – My thoughts on [person]'s offer

Hello again, Mr. / Ms. [Last name];

[Company] seems like a great company, and this particular opportunity is an exciting one for me; I'm a great fit for [Company]'s needs and it's an excellent chance for me to continue growing as an (a) _____ engineer.

Thank you for extending an offer. Included is the signed offer letter.

I look forward to working with you!

–Your first and last name
–Email signature

Resignation

Dear Mr. / Ms. [Last name];

Please accept this as my notice of resignation from [Company], effective (last day of work). I have been offered a new job opportunity, which will allow me to gain further experience. The new job is the ideal next step in my professional development.

Thank you for all the experience I have gained while working for you at [Company]. I learned a lot about engineering in the [time] years I've been here, and I appreciate the advice and support you have given me.

Please let me know what I can do to make this a smooth transition for the entire department.

Sincerely,

–Your first and last name
–Email signature

About the Author

Thomas is a licensed Mechanical Engineer who enjoys helping other engineers improve and discover their purpose to obtain the career of their dreams. He utilizes his talents and experiences to provide the best possible future for others. He is proud to be a Professional Engineer. Thomas is passionate about promoting licensure; the ethical, lawful practice of engineering; and enhancing the image of the engineering profession. He feels fortunate that he has the opportunity to practice mechanical engineering.

He is also the creator of EngineerYourCareer.net, an online resource for career support and coaching for engineers.

"Whatever engineering career you choose,
be certain it makes you happy."
—Thomas A. Anderson

References

ASCE. (2019, March 7). engineering-grades-brochure.pdf. ASCE. Retrieved from https://www.asce.org/uploadedFiles/Membership_and_ Communities/Regions_Sections_Branches/Content_Pieces/engineering-grades-brochure.pdf

Belli, G. (2017, April 6th). How Many Jobs Are Found Through Networking, Really? www.payscale.com. Retrieved November 1st, 2018, from https://www.payscale.com/career-news/2017/04/many-jobs-found-networking

Brudner, E. (2018, Feb 28). How to Sell Anything to Anybody. Hubspot. Retrieved from https://blog.hubspot.com/sales/how-to-sell-anything-to-anybody

Chapman, C. (2018, Dec 17). Student debt doubles since 2009. Retrieved from https://www.linkedin.com/feed/news/student-debt-doubles-since-2009-4791930/

Council, U. G. (2019). *Leed*. Retrieved from http://leed.usgbc.org/leed.html

Directory, I. (2018, July 9). Closing The Gap Between Men and Women in STEM. IQS Directory. Retrieved from https://www.iqsdirectory.com/blog/closing-the-gap-between-men-and-women-in-stem/

Doyle, A. (2018, October 17). How Often Do People Change Jobs. Retrieved from https://www.thebalancecareers.com/how-often-do-people-change-jobs-2060467

Elejalde, R. (2017, Nov 16). Using social media to disqualify job candidates is risky. Chicago Tribune. Retrieved from http://www.chicagotribune.com/business/ct-social-media-job-candidates-0113-biz-20160111-story.html

Erway, J. (2014). *Thinking of Turning Pro? Why Engineers Get Professional Licenses*. Engineering.com. Retrieved from http://www.engineering.com/Education/EducationArticles/ArticleID/8378/Thinking-of-Turning-Pro-Why-Engineers-Get-Professional-Licenses.aspx

Frost, A. (2017, November 14). 15 Surprising Stats on Networking and Face-to-Face Communication. Hub Spot. Retrieved from https://blog.hubspot.com/sales/face-to-face-networking-stats

Gaille, B. (2017, May 20). 15 Fear of Public Speaking Statistics. Retrieved from https://brandongaille.com/14-fear-public-speaking-statistics/

goalband.co.uk. (n.d.). 18 facts about goals and their achievement. Retrieved from www.goalband.co.uk/goal-achievement

Kelchner, L. (2018, June 29). Top Ten Effective Negotiation Skills . *Small Business – Chron.com* . Retrieved from http://smallbusiness.chron.com/top-ten-effective-negotiation-skills-31534.html

Kenton, W. (2018, Jan 19). Value Proposition. Investopedia. Retrieved from https://www.investopedia.com/terms/v/valueproposition.asp

Kramer, J. (2018, June 18). This is the 3-step process you should follow when you get a job offer. *This is the 3-step process you should follow when you get a job offer.* Fast Company. Retrieved from https://www.fastcompany.com/40585866/this-is-the-3-step-process-you-should-follow-when-you-get-a-job-offer

Muse. (2019, March 7). The 31 Best LinkedIn Profile Tips for Job Seekers. Retrieved from https://www.themuse.com/advice/the-31-best-linkedin-profile-tips-for-job-seekers

Ricci, T. (2012, December). 7 steps to landing that first job. ASME.org. Retrieved from https://www.asme.org/career-education/articles/job-hunting/7-steps-landing-first-job

Rocha, E. H. (2005). *Resume Buzz Words*. Avon, MA: Adams Media.

Segel, R. (2018, Feb 28). 4 Types of customers and How to Sell to Each of Them. Retrieved from https://www.businessknowhow.com/marketing/personalities.htm

Shields, J. (2018, Aug 30). 8 Things You Need To Know About Applicant Tracking Systems. Retrieved from https://www.jobscan.co/blog/8-things-you-need-to-know-about-applicant-tracking-systems/

Singh, H. (2017). *PMP Exam Results Report.* Deep Fried Brain. Retrieved from https://www.deepfriedbrainproject.com/2017/08/pmp-exam-result-report.html

SIXWise. (2019, March 14). How to Overcome Your Fear of Failure. *How to Overcome Your Fear of Failure.* www.sixwise.com. Retrieved from http://www.sixwise.com/newsletters/06/06/14/how_to_overcome_your_fear_of_failure.htm

Statistics, B. o. (2018). *Architecture and Engineering.* Retrieved Jan 7, 2019, from https://www.bls.gov/ooh/architecture-and-engineering/mobile/home.htm

Taylor, C. (2019, Feb 19). A Career Secret Weapon – Thank You Notes. Reuters.com. Retrieved from https://www.reuters.com/article/us-money-jobs-thankyounotes-idUSKCN1Q81FH

Training, E. (2018). *Green Associate Exam Prep.* Retrieved from http://www.everbluetraining.com/what-is-leed

Wikipedia. (2019). *List of Engineering Societies.* Wikipedia. Retrieved from https://en.wikipedia.org/wiki/List_of_engineering_societies#United_States

ATTENTION CORPORATIONS, UNIVERSITIES, COLLEGES, AND PROFESSIONAL ORGANIZATIONS:

Quantity discounts are available on bulk purchases of this book for educational, gift purposes, or as premiums for increasing magazine subscriptions or renewals. Special books or book excerpts can also be created to fit specific needs. For information contact

www.EngineerYourCareer.net

Manufactured by Amazon.ca
Bolton, ON

32642619R00107